EMERGENCY ESSENTIALS®

TIPS FOR PREPAREDNESS

EMERGENCY ESSENTIALS®

TIPS FOR PREPAREDNESS

COMPILED BY LARRY BARKDULL

SHADOW
MOUNTAIN

Photos on cover and in the book courtesy of Emergency Essentials®, Inc.
Used by permission.

Library of Congress Cataloging-in-Publication Data

    Emergency essentials' tips for preparedness / Larry Barkdull, compiler.
      p.   cm.
    Includes bibliographical references.
    ISBN 1-59038-168-8 (pbk.)
    1. Emergency management.   2. Emergency food supply   3. Emergency water supply.   4. Survival skills   I. Barkdull, Larry.

HV551.2 .E43 2003
613.6'9—dc21   2003011813

Printed in the United States of America   54459-7125
Malloy Lithographing Incorporated, Ann Arbor, MI

10   9   8   7   6   5   4   3   2   1

CONTENTS

Acknowledgments

Special thanks is extended to Don Pectol and Scott Pedersen, whose combined quarter century of expertise has made this book possible.

Appreciation is given also to David Sheets, president of Emergency Essentials®, Inc., for allowing valuable corporate resources to be dedicated to the completion of this book.

Throughout the years at Emergency Essentials®, Inc., many of its employees and departments contributed to this effort by writing and editing Insight Articles for our website www.beprepared.com. Emergency Essentials®, Inc., is grateful to all those who have made contributions. Recognition is given specifically to Matt Nettesheim, Scott Pectol, Mindy Silvia, and Jessica Hardy for helping to make the information in this book as accurate as possible and for all the extra work and insights they've given to bring it to completion. We would also like to thank the many others at Emergency Essentials® for their efforts.

Other expert writers and lecturers contributed to this book. Emergency Essentials®, Inc., is grateful for their help and recommends their works to our readers. These experts are:

Rita Bingham (author)
See page 45 for a list of her works about Preparedness & Food Storage and their usages.

Barry Crockett (author)
See page 25 for his book about emergency preparedness, 72-hour kits, and storing a year's supply.

Deloy Hendricks (Ph.D., CNS, Professor of Nutrition and Food Sciences, Utah State University)

Peggy D. Layton (author)
See page 39 for a list of her works about Preparedness & Food Storage and their usages.

LeArta Moulton (author)
See page 37 for a list of her works about Wheat, Grains & Herbs and their usages.

Marlene Petersen (author)
Author of *Marlene's Magic*.

J. Allan South (author)
Author of *The Sense of Survival*.

Vicki Tate (author)
See page 25 for a list of her works about Food and Water Storage.

CREDITS

As mentioned above, the content of this book was compiled with the cooperation of a variety of contributors. These writers are credited at the beginning of each article. In the interest of space, credits were not included for the shorter "Insights and Tips," which draw upon a combination of writings from these listed contributors, Emergency Essentials®, Inc., materials, and commonly known preparedness facts.

—Larry Barkdull
Compiling editor

INTRODUCTION

Emergency Essentials®, Inc., is one of the largest preparedness companies in the United States. Since 1987, we have been helping people prepare for emergency situations through our monthly catalogs, our website, our affiliated writers, and through our trained employees who daily answer our customers' questions. This book is an outgrowth of these combined resources and is intended to provide a  quick, easy-to-understand compilation of preparedness ideas. We hope this information helps you to prepare *before* an emergency and becomes a valuable resource during difficult times.

Emergency Preparedness Services

As a service to those who have purchased this book, Emergency Essentials®, Inc., is offering **a free copy** of a DVD/video titled *Family Preparedness Plan*. This video is a $12.00 value, which you can obtain for a reduced shipping and handling fee. You can receive your copy by calling us toll-free at **1-800-999-1863 or going to the Web at www.beprepared.com/freeDVDvid.html**

The Emergency Essentials®, Inc., website also offers other preparedness services, such as personal stories and tips from customers and proven recipes—a wealth of information! These resources will be a valuable guide as you design and implement your personal preparedness plan.

How to Use This Book

Emergency Essentials®' Tips for Preparedness is designed to give you easy-to-find, practical pointers on emergency preparedness that can be implemented immediately. This book is not intended to be encyclopedic. The chapters do not necessarily need to be read sequentially; therefore, you can open the book to any page and find valuable insights. For that reason some information is repeated because it has relevance in multiple applications. This preparedness handbook will get you started by providing information on the following general topics:

- Education and Planning
- The First Three Days of an Emergency
- Water Storage and Replenishment
- Food Storage
- Warmth, Shelter, and Clothing
- Light, Tools, and Communication
- First Aid and Sanitation
- Disaster Preparedness
- Other Preparedness Information

Accuracy

In addition to our employees' writing about many subjects over the years, other expert writers have contributed to this work and to our online library. Our customers have also offered many helpful tips. Every attempt has been made to ensure that the information in this book either originated with Emergency Essentials®, Inc., or that it has been adapted and used by permission. Anything to the contrary is purely unintentional.

Current Information

We recognize that knowledge of preparedness changes with innovation and research. What we have suggested today may change tomorrow. As an example, the invention of the light emitting diode (LED) has improved flashlights and other products. Although standard bulb flashlights and batteries will prove valuable in an emergency, today we recommend flashlights with LEDs. We hope you will consider the information in this book and "tailor-make" a preparedness plan that fits your needs.

Professional Medical Care

As you read this book, please be aware that no stated alternative treatment should be understood as recommended to take the place of accepted, professional medical care. Your first course of action should always be to seek professional knowledge, advice, and treatment. In compiling this information, we have targeted the broad principles of preparation and assume that you know your own toleration for certain foods and individual needs. If you are in doubt, consult a professional.

Feeling of Confidence

Above every other consideration, being prepared gives you a feeling of confidence. When an emergency situation arises, you are better prepared to weather the storm and be of service to people in need. We hope this informative book helps you to begin or improve your preparedness plan.

—David E. Sheets
—Don W. Pectol
—Scott N. Pedersen
—Matt R. Nettesheim
Emergency Essentials®, Inc.
Executive Management Team

www.beprepared.com
www.emergencyessentials.com
1-800-999-1863

CHAPTER ONE

EDUCATION AND PLANNING

Could It Happen to You?

Jane was standing in her kitchen feeding her children breakfast, *quake* hurrying them along so that they would not miss the school bus. The January mornings had been particularly cold and dark. Suddenly, she felt the floor move as though it was elastic. Her first thought was that a construction truck had rumbled down the street. Then a shock shot through the house, and her knees buckled. She grabbed for the countertop to steady herself. The walls bent crazily, and pictures, china, and figurines began to fall. Six-year-old Emily cried out from the bathroom, but Jane could not move. Eight-year-old Collin crawled under his chair and covered his head with his hands. Within a few moments, food was scattered all over the kitchen; the water main had broken; the electricity was out; and phone service was disrupted.

Bob arrived at work at 7:50 A.M., the way he always had for the last twelve years. He had received raises, perks, promotions, and now he was in line to be transferred and named to a high-profile *downsizing* position. So that morning nothing could have shocked him more than being informed that he was part of a massive corporate downsizing. The first thought that flashed through his mind was, "Is my family ready for this?"

Fire

> *Beverly was awakened at 3:45 A.M. by the singing of the smoke alarm. Groggily, she climbed out of bed, donned her robe, and stumbled into the hall. Thick smoke was billowing up out of the stairwell. Suddenly awake, she raced into her children's bedrooms, gathered them into her arms, and blindly stumbled through the front door and out into the street. There, as she huddled with her little ones, watching everything they owned being consumed in the inferno, she thought, "I never thought this could happen to me."*

We all hope that emergency situations such as these will never happen to us. But we only need follow the news to see that disruptive circumstances occur both frequently and indiscriminately.

BE PREPARED

These two simple words have an amazing range of meaning. To one person the phrase can mean, "Get ready for dinner"; to another person it can mean the detailed planning of an ascent of Mt. Everest. In this book, "be prepared" means provident preparation for unforeseen occurrences, large and small. These can include anything from running out of gas in your car to being prepared for a hurricane.

Matt Hufford experienced September 11, 2001, inside New York City's World Trade Center. Following that tragic and terrifying experience, he said, "After being in a life-threatening situation like that, I can tell you, the only emotion that compares with the fear of death is the fear that results from being unprepared. I promised myself that I wouldn't subject my family members to that fear."

An inner confidence results when a person knows he has done his best to prepare. **The place to begin is to obtain information.** We have all experienced that "ah-ha" feeling when we discover a simple solution to a seemingly large task. Maybe someone gives you an insight or a tip or a bit of practical information; suddenly you feel empowered and motivated. The fog of ignorance dissipates in the face of warm rays of understanding.

"On July 24th some time ago, I was in my office in Orem, Utah, when I received a phone call from a woman in Southern California. As we were talking, an earthquake shook her home, and she became very afraid. I did my best to instruct her. "Get under a doorway," I said, trying to calm her.

When the quaking ended, she ceased to panic, thanked me for my assistance, and went to assess the damage. I sat back, took a deep breath, and mused about the singularity of the experience.

Within hours, one of my employees came into my office and told me that a customer had just experienced a flash flood in Phoenix, Arizona. The street where she lived had literally turned into a dangerous river. After the employee left, I pondered what I had experienced that day. A feeling of smug security came over me. I thought, How grateful I am to live in Orem, Utah, where things like this rarely happen.

Within a few hours a policeman came to our corporate headquarters and told us that we would have to immediately evacuate the building. A nearby chemical plant had caught fire, and there was a possibility of an explosion taking place. When I then arrived home, a short distance from my office, another police officer was informing our neighborhood that the area had become unsafe and that we may have to leave until the emergency was contained.

The lesson I learned that day has stuck with me over the years: No one is immune from all danger, and no one lives in a place that is totally free of the unexpected.

Don W. Pectol

If we are to confidently work our way through emergencies and disasters, knowledge is crucial. To the degree you prepare, you equip yourself to reduce or avoid serious consequences. Of course there are myriad voices offering endless advice. Your responsibility is to arm yourself with knowledge from reliable sources, then to adapt all that information to your specific family needs and conditions.

The 72-hour emergency kit is a wonderful model for preparedness. A 72-hour emergency kit is a mobile backpack filled with necessary supplies to sustain life for three days. It can be made for comprehensive needs or for lightweight travel. It is easy to assemble and quick to grab when needed.

Why 72 hours? Many people are apathetic about preparedness or they are not sure where to begin. They are so overwhelmed that they become discouraged before they begin. Others are frustrated by contradictory advice, not sure whose ideas to follow. Still others do nothing, figuring, erroneously, that if trouble comes, the government or an emergency disaster agency will rush to their rescue. Such organizations perform marvelous services, but when large populations are relying solely upon them, it is virtually impossible for them to meet all individual needs. The Federal Emergency Management Agency (FEMA) has stated, *If a disaster threatens your community, local government and disaster-relief organizations will try to help you. But you need to be prepared as well. Local officials may be overwhelmed after a major disaster, and emergency response personnel may not be able to reach you right away.* What you do to prepare can make a difference.

Most relief organizations would need approximately three days (72 hours) to mobilize and be able to help you. Because disasters can happen at any time and to any surrounding, making a 72-hour survival kit for each of your family members should be a high priority. Do your part by having three days' food, water, and supplies.

GETTING STARTED NOW

Too many people make the mistake in thinking that emergencies only happen to "other folks." Beyond the subject of disasters, being prepared should be a part of your normal provident living. Don't become overwhelmed. Start with small goals and work consistently. Here are a few ideas to help you get started with your preparedness plan.

- Establish a modest preparedness budget. Make it a priority and work at it the best you can. Start with a few items, such as: a 72-hour kit, emergency candles, a sleeping bag, and a first aid kit or an emergency bag. Then budget enough money monthly to keep adding to your stores of emergency supplies. Working toward being prepared truly brings peace of mind.

- Get your information from reliable sources. Most sensible programs will coincide with other reputable sources such as books, community preparation, and church or government programs. Don't let anyone scare you into thinking that it has to be done all at once or that you must incur heavy debt to achieve your goals.

- That which would be required to sustain life for three days can be easily multiplied for planning long-term storage needs.

- Be consistent. Within a short time you will have the necessary supplies and equipment to take care of yourself, family members, and others.

- Think investment, not expense! Think practically when it comes to assembling a food storage program. Buy the basics and learn to use them. Buy foods that you can rotate and eat regularly instead of storing foods that are unknown to you and that you have never eaten. Buy emergency materials that can be used for other activities such as Scouting events, camping adventures, and family road trips. Take care of what you purchase and learn to not waste. The point is, do something and do not procrastinate. An unknown writer said, "On the plains of hesitation bleach the bones of countless millions, who on the dawn of victory rested, and resting died."

Whether or not we choose to believe that life is dynamic, changes and challenges will come to each of us. How we prepare today can help ensure that we experience a soft landing. Start with a simple plan and use wisdom as you implement that plan. The articles and tips in this book will help you to tailor-make a preparedness program that fits your way of life.

CHAPTER TWO

THE FIRST THREE DAYS OF AN EMERGENCY

How to Prepare and for What

Floods, fires, earthquakes, hurricanes, tornadoes, civil unrest—any of a number of emergencies could strike at any time. Government and relief agencies estimate that relief efforts can take up to three days to reach those in need. In such cases, your 72-hour kit could mean the difference between life and death. Federal and local government and religious leaders recommend that you should prepare and personalize a kit for each member of your family by including clothing, personal documents, medications, and other essential emergency provisions, such as food, water, light, warmth, and shelter.

Being prepared will allow you and your family to avoid fear and enjoy a sense of security. Preparedness also prevents much of the inconvenience and loss that might ordinarily accompany a crisis that takes you by surprise. You must not solely rely on outside agencies to rescue you in a time of disaster. You must be ready to act in a positive way for you and your family.

EMERGENCY KIT CHECKLISTS

Here are some basic emergency preparedness considerations to keep in mind as you personalize your family's preparedness plan and your emergency kit. (You will find more detail as you read this book.)

EDUCATION CHECKLIST

- ❑ Take first aid or CPR class and read educational publications
- ❑ Anticipate what might happen and how to respond
- ❑ Establish a communication network for your immediate and extended family
- ❑ Have a well-practiced evacuation plan
- ❑ Learn how to administer first aid
- ❑ Own (and read) an outdoor survival skills reference book
- ❑ Prepare a list of important phone numbers and addresses
- ❑ Take part in your community preparedness and response events

WATER CHECKLIST

- ❑ Prepackaged drinking water pouches and small boxed drinking water
- ❑ Some kind of water replenishing system—water filter, purifier, solar still, distiller, etc.
- ❑ 5-gallon boxed water in metallized bags, water storage barrels, jugs, and bottles

FOOD CHECKLIST

- ❑ A supply of high-calorie, compressed food bars
- ❑ Ready-to-Eat Meals (MREs)
- ❑ Freeze-dried backpacking meals
- ❑ Candy, desserts, and stress-relieving foods, such as snacks (jerky, granola bars, trail mix, soup mixes, fruit leather, high-energy bars, just-add-water meals such as instant breakfasts, etc.)

Shelter and Bedding Checklist

- ❑ Tent, ground cloth, or tarp
- ❑ Recreational vehicle or camper
- ❑ Sleeping bags and insulated pads
- ❑ Wool blankets and fleece liners
- ❑ Newspaper and cardboard for bedding or ground padding

Clothing and Warmth Checklist

- ❑ Appropriate day/night clothing for your surrounding area and climate
- ❑ Extra essential clothing, such as underwear, socks, T-shirts, etc.
- ❑ Parka, poncho, jacket, rain gear
- ❑ Shoes or boots (Use boots in cold weather, or in earthquake, tornado, or rough debris areas)
- ❑ Socks made of synthetic or woolen material—not cotton
- ❑ Hat and gloves made of synthetic material
- ❑ Disposable hand and body warm packs or reheaters
- ❑ Emergency reflective bag or blanket
- ❑ Portable gas or electric heater with necessary fire starters
- ❑ Firemaking skills

Fuel and Cooking Checklist

- ❑ A small stove and appropriate liquid or pressurized canister fuel
- ❑ Fold-out stove that uses Sterno®, Eco Fuel®, Trioxane fuel bars, gelled alcohol, etc.
- ❑ MRE heater (no matches or fuel required) ✱
- ❑ Fire starters—windproof/waterproof matches, lighter kit,

magnesium block starter, steel wool, 9-volt battery, magnifying glass, and road flares
- ❏ Portable cook sets and utensils
- ❏ Clean-up soap and scrubbing pads

Lighting Checklist

- ❏ Lamps, lanterns, and extra fuel
- ❏ Candles, LED flashlights, head lamps, incandescent light bulbs, light sticks
- ❏ Extra batteries
- ❏ Fire starters (see list above)

Communication Checklist

- ❏ Solar or electric battery charger with rechargeable batteries
- ❏ Light sticks, strobe light, signal mirror, back-country beacon
- ❏ Cellular phone, walkie-talkie, access to ham or CB radio
- ❏ Notebook and pencil or marker
- ❏ Road or aerial flares
- ❏ Whistle with neck cord
- ❏ Weather, short-wave, AM/FM radios

First Aid and Special Medications Checklist

Make personalized first aid kit with the following:

- ❏ Different-sized bandages and sterile dressings
- ❏ Gauze wraps
- ❏ Children's medications for fever, pain, special needs
- ❏ Personal medications for diabetes, heart conditions, allergies, etc.
- ❏ Burn-relieving gel and dressings
- ❏ "OB" pads for large wounds
- ❏ Scissors, EMT shears, tweezers, hemostats, forceps, clamps
- ❏ Antibiotic creams such as Neosporin®
- ❏ Insect repellent and calamine lotion

❑ Sun block, lip balm, petroleum jelly
❑ Sanitizers, antiseptic wipes or towelettes, antibacterial soap, sterilized water pouches for cleaning or eyewash, Campho Phenique®
❑ Snakebite kit
❑ Latex or vinyl gloves
❑ CPR shield, mouth-to-mouth shield
❑ Instant ice and heat packs
❑ Instant relief medication such as aspirin (or other pain reliever), cold, flu, cough medications
❑ Thermometer
❑ Splint, ace wraps, triangular bandages with safety pins
❑ Easily identifiable carrying bag for your kit
❑ Sting relief medications or swabs

SANITATION AND TOILETRIES CHECKLIST

❑ Personal comfort kit (include antibacterial soap, toothbrush, floss, toothpaste, chewing gum, mints, comb, tissue, razor, zippered plastic bags, mouthwash, and other needed items)
❑ Portable toilet, toilet paper, and enzymes
❑ Extra garbage bags
❑ Sundries: shampoo, sanitizers, lotion, etc.
❑ Privacy shelter, shovel, or trowel
❑ Towel, washcloth, wipes, laundry soap, and bucket
❑ Feminine hygiene supplies, nursing pads, etc.

TOOLS AND EQUIPMENT CHECKLIST

❑ Fishing and hunting equipment
❑ Ax or hatchet and hammer
❑ Folding saw, bow saw, or ring (pocket) saw
❑ Prybar or crowbar
❑ Small shovel, pick, or garden trowel

- ❑ Household tools: screwdriver set, pliers, measuring tape, adjustable crescent wrench, etc.
- ❑ Garbage bags
- ❑ Multifunctional pocketknife
- ❑ Knife sharpener
- ❑ Length of strong rope
- ❑ Gas and water shut-off wrenches
- ❑ Good quality compass and orienteering guide
- ❑ Cell phone or 2-way radios
- ❑ Road and backcountry maps
- ❑ Miscellaneous repair kits (sewing kit, shoelaces, rubber patch kit, duct tape, plastic sheeting, bailing wire, etc.)
- ❑ Protective gloves (leather, latex, etc.)

PACKS AND TRANSPORTATION CHECKLIST

- ❑ Backpacks, kid carrier, and daypacks
- ❑ Duffle bags
- ❑ Suitcase with wheels and handle
- ❑ Plastic buckets
- ❑ Garbage can with wheels
- ❑ Bicycle with pack
- ❑ Wheelbarrow
- ❑ Large stroller
- ❑ Wagon (large enough to carry 50 pounds)
- ❑ Hand truck or dolly
- ❑ Vehicles (car, truck, RV, boat, bicycle, motorcycle, camper, trailer)

AUTOMOBILE PREPAREDNESS CHECKLIST

- ❑ Bottled water for drinking and cooking—2 gallons minimum—or drinking water pouches or Aqua Blox®
- ❑ Fire extinguisher
- ❑ Flashlight with good batteries (LED flashlights are best)

- High-calorie food bars—
  2,400 to 3,600 calories—
  or food of your choice
- Tool kit
- Long, heavy-duty jumper cables
- Tow rope
- Windshield scraper
- Flat-tire kit, including jack, lug
  wrench, air supply
- Short rubber hose for siphoning
- Waterproof matches and emergency candles
- First aid kit with burn supplies and a first aid manual
- Toilet paper
- Maps and a compass
- Cell phone with recharging device
- CB radio
- AM/FM radio that is independent of the car
- Road and signal flares
- Extra batteries
- Wool-blend blanket or emergency blanket or sleeping bag
- Small cook stove and fuel with container to cook in
- Small shovel or trowel
- Eating utensils
- Canned heat
- Small sharp knife or pocketknife
- Facial tissue, paper towels
- Large size plastic garbage bags (use for weather protection or
  as a container, or cut a hole and wear as a poncho)
- Safety pins
- Pain reliever
- Paper and pencil/pen
- Long-range whistle
- Coins for pay telephone

- ❏ Wire and/or string cord
- ❏ Duct tape and electrical tape
- ❏ Maintain at least 1/2 tank of fuel
- ❏ Leather gloves
- ❏ Hand and body warmers

SECURITY AND PROTECTION CHECKLIST

- ❏ Know how to shut off electricity (main breaker)
- ❏ Know how to shut off gas and water and have proper tools
- ❏ Fire escape ladder for each upper story bedroom
- ❏ Inventory list of belongings (photos for insurance claims)
- ❏ Duct tape and plastic sheeting
- ❏ Adequate personal and home protection, including security system
- ❏ Smoke and carbon monoxide alarms, fire extinguisher (ABC class)
- ❏ Latex gloves, gas masks, surgical masks

CHILDREN'S NEEDS CHECKLIST

- ❏ Diapers, wipes, formula, appropriate food (cereal, strained foods, etc.)
- ❏ Children's pain and fever medications, baby bottles, sundries, Calamine lotion
- ❏ Extra bedding and blankets
- ❏ Up-to-date vaccinations
- ❏ Fun foods and toys for stress relief (sugar cereal, candy, etc.)

STRESS RELIEVERS CHECKLIST

- ❏ Journal, notepad, and pen
- ❏ Scriptures, songbook, reading material
- ❏ Radio, Walkman® with inspirational or entertaining music, motivational or talk tapes.

- ❑ Camera and film and extra batteries
- ❑ Toys, ball, game cards, coloring books, and crayons or markers

MONEY CHECKLIST

- ❑ Cash—$20 to $200 in small denominations, including change for making phone calls
- ❑ Credit cards for hotels, gas, and food
- ❑ ATM card for extra cash
- ❑ Small calculator, pencil, and paper
- ❑ Spare house keys and car keys

IMPORTANT DOCUMENTS CHECKLIST

- ❑ Special family photos
- ❑ Identification and legal papers
- ❑ Insurance policies
- ❑ Financial portfolios
- ❑ Deeds and titles
- ❑ Wills
- ❑ All financial account numbers
- ❑ Credit card information
- ❑ Copies of important contracts, certificates, funds
- ❑ Make sure family members are properly immunized and that each has received a current tetanus shot

CHAPTER THREE

WATER STORAGE AND REPLENISHMENT

The Importance of Water

by Scott Pedersen, Vicki Tate, and Barry Crockett

Next to air, water is man's most critical need. Our bodies are about 80 percent liquid, and dehydration of only 6 to 8 percent of the body's weight results in decreased body efficiency. We lose water in three ways: perspiration, respiration, and urination. In the summer heat, we lose about one gallon of water per day. Within three days of sustained water depletion or loss, the body and organs can experience severe damage. Blood loses its density; the potential for heart attack and stroke increases; the kidneys begin to fail; and the mind begins to hallucinate. It is obvious, then, that in a challenging situation, finding, storing, or treating water is critical.

Not only is water essential to maintain health, it is also important for use in cooking, personal hygiene, sanitation, cleaning wounds, sprouting seeds, and reconstituting dehydrated foods, including baby formula. Because water is so essential for survival, it is necessary to have both a stored supply of drinking water and a way to treat water for your continuing needs.

HOW MUCH WATER DO YOU NEED?

Store as much "drinkable" water as is convenient to maintain. The average water need for an average-size person in an average climate is approximately one gallon of water per day (two quarts for drinking and two quarts for cooking). Most preparedness experts recommend storing 14 gallons of "drinkable" water per person. When you consider that the average person uses about 100 gallons of water per day for drinking, bathing, laundry, watering lawns, etc., it is evident that one gallon per person per day is minimal. But in an emergency, you can survive. We recommend that you store more water, if possible. Water is inexpensive to store; the biggest problem is finding space to store it.

CONTAINERS

It is important that you use only new, high quality, food-grade plastic containers designed for water storage. Do not use old bleach containers, plastic milk jugs, fuel cans, paint buckets, or antifreeze containers to store drinking water. There are many other storage options that are safer and more reliable. We recommend using durable, dark-colored (blue, green) polyplastic, polyethylene containers that  restrict light. This helps controls algae and bacteria growth.

Most water containers come in 1-, 5-, 7-, 15-, 30-, and 55-gallon sizes. Consider storing the bulk of your water in 55-gallon, polyethylene (plastic) water drums. These containers take up a small amount of space for the quantity of water they hold. In addition to storing water in the larger 55-gallon drums, you might also consider using two to six containers that store between five and fifteen gallons in case you need to transport water. Water weighs eight pounds per gallon, and transporting a 440-pound, 55-gallon drum would be almost impossible without the use of a hand truck. Likewise, the 1-gallon containers or the 2- to 3-liter bottles don't hold enough water and would require that you make many trips to a water source. The 5- or 15-gallon containers can be easily transported in a wheelbarrow or a child's wagon. The 5-gallon metallized bag in a box is another good choice for storing portable water because it is nonporous (odor control), and it prevents light from entering. Beyond these transportation problems, however, the 2-liter pop bottles make good containers.

STORING YOUR WATER

Heavy containers should always be stored close to ground level and secured to prevent breakage or possible injury in the event of an earthquake. Be sure to store your water in plastic containers away from any harmful chemicals or foul-smelling products because plastic tends to absorb odors. Avoid setting water storage containers directly on a cement floor because they will leach moisture from the cement that will end up in your water. Elevate the containers by placing them on boards or pallets. Rotate your water at least annually to ensure freshness, taste, and purity. Pastel or white colored containers need to be stored in a dark room or pantry to avoid being exposed to light. If you cannot store containers in a dark room, cover containers to keep out light.

WATER CONTAMINANTS

In order to understand how to make water *potable* (suitable for drinking), we must first understand what contaminants make water *unsuitable* for drinking. Most surface water (rivers, lakes, streams, reservoirs) contains some types of microorganisms (protozoa, bacteria, viruses) and/or pollutants (chemicals, foul odors, sewage, spilled fuel).

MICROORGANISMS

Microorganisms are living microscopic cells that, when consumed, can cause diseases such as dysentery, cholera, typhoid, and hepatitis. Some microorganisms can even cause death for those with weak immune systems (children, elderly, sick).

Protozoa (the largest of all microorganisms) include such parasites as giaridia lamblia and cryptosporidium. Bacteria (medium-size microorganisms) include E. coli, vibrio cholerae, campylobacter, and salmonella, all of which are found in human and animal waste. Most common microorganism contamination occurs in food preparation and processing, both at home and in the food industry (especially when workers don't wash their hands after using the bathroom). Viruses are the smallest of all the microorganisms. They include hepatitis A and B, Norwalk virus, rotavirus, poliovirus, and echovirus.

POLLUTANTS

Pollutants generally fall into two categories: manmade and natural. Natural pollutants include water contaminants such as minerals (salts) and heavy metals. Manmade pollutants are introduced into water from such sources as manufacturing plants, poor waste and disposal management, air pollution, and so on. Most often these pollutants are chemicals, fuels, or sewage or their byproducts. These pollutants can cause water to taste foul, and they can cause physical ailments or death.

HOW TO MAKE YOUR WATER SAFE TO DRINK (POTABLE)

For a long-term emergency plan you need to have a method to make questionable water potable and safe. You should also have a method of replenishing your drinking water. There are three primary ways to convert "raw," undrinkable water into safe, potable water: purification, filtration, and distillation (solar). Each method has its advantages and disadvantages. Start with the cleanest, least salty, and least polluted water you can find. Realize that no method is perfect and sometimes combining methods is the best solution.

Method 1—Water Purification

Culinary water (tap water) can be used for long-term storage. Guaranteeing that culinary water is bacteria-free water is difficult. **You do not need to treat culinary water at the time you store it. The time to treat your stored water is after you've stored it and just BEFORE**

you use it. Why? Purifying chemicals eventually wear out, and bacteria can begin to grow.

There are three general ways to make surface water free from disease-causing microorganisms: 1) add extreme heat to the water (i.e., boiling and distilling), 2) add disinfectant (chemical or silver), and 3) expose water to ultraviolet light.

Boiling

Historically, boiling water has been the main way to disinfect water from microorganisms because it kills them all if done correctly. Boiling water for at least three minutes will kill all viruses. Bacteria and protozoa are dead at the first bubbles, but viruses need a little more time. There are some drawbacks to boiling water. First, boiling can require a lot of fuel and cooking equipment. Second, you must consider the long cool-down period. Third, some of the water will evaporate before it is ready to drink. Fourth, the water will still have particulate substances in it, so you should use a clean handkerchief to filter it before drinking. Last, boiling water does not eliminate pollutants, poor taste, or foul odors. In fact, boiling can give water a stale taste. To improve the taste of boiled water, transfer water from one container to another several times after boiling.

Chemical Treatments

Two primary chemicals are used for purifying water: iodine and chlorine. These two chemicals are lightweight, inexpensive, and relatively easy to use.

Iodine has been found to be very effective against viruses, bacteria, and protozoa with the exception of cryptosporidium. Iodine generally takes about thirty minutes to purify and leaves a flavor some people do not enjoy. This taste can be improved by adding a sugar-based drink or juice mix. The colder the water you wish to treat, the more time is required to disinfect it. Because iodine is absorbed into dirt and debris, which is found in water, its purification dosage varies. Pregnant women and people with thyroid conditions should not drink water purified with iodine. Additionally, iodine is a short-term water-purification solution and should not be used regularly for longer than three months. Iodine does not change the clarity of water but it does change its taste. A good product is Potable Aqua® iodine purification tablets. Just add two tablets per liter of water.

Chlorine bleach can also be used to purify water. FEMA, the Clorox ® company, and the Red Cross have recommended using Clorox Bleach to purify raw water. The Red Cross pamphlet states, " . . . use regular household bleach that contains 5.25% sodium hypochlorite. Do not use scented bleaches, colorsafe bleaches, or bleaches with added cleaners." When using bleach to purify, "add 16 drops of bleach per gallon of water (1 drop per cup), stir, and let stand for 30 minutes. If the water does not have a slight bleach odor, repeat the dosage and let stand another 15 minutes." Another way to use chlorine is in predetermined amounts (tablets). Drop the prescribed amount in a liter of water and let sit for thirty minutes. The tablet will dissolve and permeate the water, killing any microorganisms. Chlorine tablets can also kill cryptosporidium, but it takes four hours to do its work. Chlorine leaves a somewhat objectionable taste and smell to your water. Letting the water sit for an hour or so after treatment will remove that taste and odor. It also helps to add a sugar-based drink or juice mix to the treated water. The process of chlorination will cause dirt and debris to settle to the bottom of the water container and make the water visually clearer. If the household bleach is more than six months old or the chlorine tablet doesn't dissolve, it may not have enough potency to disinfect. You must be very careful if you attempt to use household bleach as a purifier. Chlorine is very poisonous, and adding too much can cause illness, internal organ damage, or even death. If you decide to use bleach or chlorine tablets, be sure to add it just before you intend to use your water, NOT at the time you store it.

Other Water Purification Methods

Silver is a natural purifier, and throughout the centuries, people in many countries have used pure silver to disinfect water. Additionally, silver has been and is being used therapeutically for sicknesses and infections, and as an antibiotic (although some controversy continues as to its actual effectiveness). In the United States it has recently been accepted as an agent for water purification.

Ultraviolet (UV). Because electricity is required to generate ultraviolet light, it is mainly used as a home filtration method for water; it is not typically practical otherwise. Water enters an ultraviolet-lighted chamber and swirls around a high-output, low-pressure mercury vapor lamp, which emits powerful ultraviolet light. The energy components of microorganisms absorb the light energy, which disrupts their DNA, preventing them from reproducing. UV lighting literally sterilizes the microorganisms, rendering them ineffective in making one sick. UV lighting adds no chemicals to change water's taste. Beyond requiring electricity, UV methods demand some method of filtration to remove dirt, debris, chemicals, tastes, and odors. UV purification is considered a good "stage" of the purification process, but it is not complete by itself.

Method 2—Water Filtration

Filtration simply means to strain out the impurities from a water source. The larger the impurity particulate, the easier it is to filter. The opposite is true also; the smaller the impurity particulate, the harder it is to remove. Thus, the size of the filter pore and the durability of the filtering element are important to the filter's longevity and effectiveness. Most filtering elements are made of ceramic, glass fiber, hard-block carbon, or materials that resemble compressed surgical paper.

Ceramic elements (most expensive, durable, and maintainable) have the smallest pore size (0.1-0.5 microns) and are used by some of the leading potable water filtering companies in the world. Portable ceramic filters boast an impressive list of long-term users, such as the International Red Cross, the World Health Organization, the armed forces (USA,

Germany, Portugal, Switzerland), the United Nations, and the FBI. Ceramic elements can filter only free floating particulates and micro-organisms. They do not remove chemicals, foul tastes, odors, or pollutants.

Glass fiber elements and compressed surgical paper (mildly expen-sive, medium durability, and usually not reusable) also have small pores (0.2–1.0 microns). Like ceramic filters, they remove only particulates and microorganisms, and they do not remove pollutants. These are effective, low-cost filtering elements suitable for home, backpacking, and camping needs, but they are not good for long-term storage because they can develop mold and mildew and do not hold together well when they are cleaned.

Hard-block carbon elements (less expensive, brittle, and not clean-able) have a small but still effective pore size (0.4–2.0 microns). They are also used as absorption filters. Carbon is the only filtration method that reduces chemical content, poor taste, odors, and many pollutants. Because carbon is only mildly effective in filtering out particulates and microorganisms, it is mostly used as a second- or third-stage filter in home and potable water use. It is seldom effective as a stand-alone filtering unit.

Method 3—Solar Still

Solar stills operate upon the "greenhouse effect." A clear plastic barrier (a plastic bag, ground cloth, or plastic grocery sack) is placed over a "source," such as soil, tree branches, or other organic materials. The sun's (solar) energy passes through the barrier and heats the source material. Moisture from the source vaporizes, rises, and then condenses on the underside of the plastic barrier. The moisture can then be col-lected as drinkable water. Solar stills are capable of distilling almost any tainted water, even sea water. Solar stills can condense drinkable water from practically anything that contains moisture. The only source materials from which it cannot distill drinkable water are materials that give off toxins, such as fluids that contain high amounts of chemicals, radiator fluids, and fuels.

Solar stills are easy to construct and require only two essential components: 1) a container to catch the water and 2) a large sheet of clear plastic (from 6' x 6' to 9' x 9'). Optional items include a long plastic drinking tube with end cap, a small shovel, and duct tape.

Solar stills are inexpensive to make, and most of their component parts can be purchased at a hardware store. However, solar stills should be your last method for finding drinkable water during an emergency. This distilling process is extremely slow and only small amounts can be collected daily. A solar still is good when you have exhausted other methods.

PLAN AHEAD TO COMBINE METHODS

Combining methods of obtaining and purifying water can make water safe to drink and better tasting. Become aware of your area's surrounding surface water and determine what methods would be best to make that water safe to drink. Educate yourself to know what works, what doesn't, and how you could get more drinkable water if you needed it.

The time to store water is now. The water that we take for granted becomes absolutely critical in an emergency. Water is not an item you can afford to overlook in your preparedness program.

Vickie Tate is the coauthor of *Cookin' with Home Storage* and *Designing a Livable Food and Water Storage* (an audio cassette).

Barry Crockett is the author of *A Years' Supply* and *How to Assemble a 72-Hour Emergency Kit and Disaster Action Guide*.

WATER INSIGHTS AND TIPS

GLASS CONTAINERS FOR WATER STORAGE

Glass containers can break in some emergencies. If you use glass containers, be careful where and how you store them. Place newspaper between glass containers to pad and protect. Protect containers from falling off a shelf by nailing a thin strip of wood or plastic on the front edge.

WATER GOING FLAT

Studies show that if water is bacteria-free and is stored in clean, food-grade containers, away from sunlight, it will remain safe for many months. However, you should rotate your water at least every 6–12 months. Stored water often "goes flat" and loses its taste. This occurs because of the oxidation that takes place as the water sits. You can improve the taste by pouring the water back and forth between containers to aerate it, or you can use a mixer pitcher or a hand-operated eggbeater.

Store some flavorings such as fruit drink powders to add to your water to mask objectionable tastes.

OTHER SOURCES OF WATER

Remember, you have several sources of water in your home that you can use in most emergencies: the hot water heater, ice in the freezer, the toilet tanks—not the bowl. (Don't use water from a tank that contains disinfectant. That is poisonous.) Use liquids (juice, milk) in the refrigerator first, then resort to other stored water. If the emergency has caused the water to become impure, these sources should not be used. For cleaning purposes, you can also use water from a properly maintained swimming pool, or you can collect and purify or filter rain from rain gutters or buckets.

If you have a well, you should still store some water. You cannot depend entirely on that source. Earthquakes, for example, often change water tables or damage wells.

WATER CONSERVATION

The average person uses about 100 gallons of water a day! How is this possible? Flushing toilets, showering and bathing, washing laundry and dishes, and cooking and drinking require more water than you might think. For instance:

- A five-minute shower uses 25–50 gallons (calculated at 5–10 gallons a minute).

- A typical bathtub holds 35 gallons of water.
- Many toilets use six to seven gallons of water per flush.
- Running water continuously while brushing your teeth can waste two gallons of water.
- An automatic washing machine may use from 36–60 gallons of water for a full cycle.

WATER-SAVING TIPS

- Rather than running the water continuously, fill a glass half way with water to wet your toothbrush and to rinse your mouth.
- Limit showers to five minutes or less. While you wait for the water to warm up, fill a bucket with the cooler water and use it later to water your plants.
- When taking a bath, only fill the tub halfway.
- Fill a one-gallon plastic container with water and put it in the toilet tank to displace one gallon of water (or use a brick encased in a zippered plastic bag).
- Plant lawn grass that requires little watering, such as a variety planted in dry climates.
- Check faucets, hoses, and other water devices for leaks.
- Water your lawn and garden only between the hours of 9 P.M. and 9 A.M. to minimize evaporation.
- During emergencies, recycle your used bathing and laundry water for flushing the toilet or mopping your floors. (Don't use water containing cleansers like bleach or borax to water plants.) Use disposable plates, cups, and eating utensils to avoid having to wash dishes.
- When rotating your water supply, use the discarded water for your lawn, garden, and household plants.

CHAPTER FOUR

FOOD STORAGE

Why Long-Term Storage?

America is the land of plenty, a place of security and shelter for its citizens. Would there ever come a time when we would need to use food storage here? Research has shown that the average American household has less than a week's supply of food on hand. This is also the case with the average American supermarket. Without becoming paranoid or panicked, we can think of many valid reasons to put away extra food. Of course we hear of natural disasters, but think of other disruptive events that are beyond our control: loss of electricity; unemployment; illness or injury;  high medical bills; etc. Unfortunately, most Americans are only a paycheck away from financial need. Having extra food stored is a form of insurance for you and your family.

A WISE INVESTMENT

Food storage becomes more than good insurance if you practice storing what you use and using what you store. It becomes an investment. Your food storage program should be a "lifestyle" food program rather than a "make do" program. Using and rotating your food storage on a regular basis maintains your original investment because nothing is wasted. If you are accustomed to eating the food you have stored, you will be better prepared to use it during times of emergency. Always start with the basics: water, grains, legumes, milk, sugar, salt, cooking oil, and garden seeds. These are the basics for your long-term food storage plan. They have been proven to sustain life. They store longer than most foods, and they contain life-giving nutrition. These basics are typically inexpensive and within the budget of most people.

A FEELING OF SECURITY

Having a supply of stored food provides a feeling of confidence and security that comes from knowing your family will have food to eat no matter what happens with the economy, your employment, or the outside world. Confidence in times of crisis can be your greatest asset and bring you and your family peace of mind. Maintaining an adequate food supply for your family should be a major part of your economic planning, and it could possibly be your key to survival.

SELF-RELIANCE

Having a supply of stored food also helps you to become self-reliant. You are better prepared to endure times of adversity without becoming dependent upon institutions or other people. If a life-altering event were to occur, and if you were forced to temporarily leave your home or change your living habits, you could do so with minimal discomfort.

As an example, in the mid-1950s a flood occurred in Northern California. Many bridges were washed out, and supplies that would have been arriving at grocery stores were cut off. One person rushed into a grocery store and purchased all the milk, much more than he needed. His was an act of selfishness motivated by fear. An individual who prepares ahead of time can reduce his fear and even be in a situation to share his storage with others. This is truly the self-reliance and preparedness spirit, one of helping and sharing.

Basic Foods and Better Health

by Rita Bingham

Throughout history, many people have experienced improved health when they were forced to live on simple, basic foods. These people have actually thrived. Commercially prepared foods are almost always filled with chemical additives, colorings, and flavorings. Because our bodies can more easily utilize basic foods, they should always be our first choice. To get the best possible nutrition, start with the basics listed below. Use these on a daily basis, and add the others when you can afford them.

GRAINS

Wheat is indeed a versatile grain. Used in appetizers, main dishes, salads, snacks, and desserts, wheat adds flavor, texture, and protein as well as many important vitamins and minerals. Fiber in the American diet is a popular subject these days, and whole wheat is one of the best-tasting and easiest-to-use sources of fiber. Cracked wheat requires only three minutes of cooking time and can be added to almost any recipe.

If you are allergic to wheat, learn to use such grains as brown rice, corn, quinoa, amaranth, buckwheat, rye, triticale, spelt, kamut, whole oats, millet, and barley.

DRY BEANS (LEGUMES)

Beans, peas, and lentils are some of the best food bargains. They are important staple foods for over half the world's population. Most of us are familiar with pinto and kidney beans and homemade split pea soup, but there are many other ways to use legumes.

With advance preparation, beans can be added to many last-minute meals. Beans can be cooked, sprouted, cracked, or even ground to fine flour (that also cooks in only three minutes!), then frozen until ready for use to preserve the nutrients.

Legumes are great mixers as well as meat extenders. They can be mixed with other vegetables, used to "beef" up a salad, or served as dips and sandwich spreads. Legumes are a rich source of protein, iron, calcium, phosphorus, thiamin, and potassium. When combined with grains, they supply all the amino acids necessary to form a complete protein. Some of the best are garbanzo, black, small white, soy, mung, pink, red, lentils, and peas.

NON-FAT DRY MILK

Good quality, dehydrated, non-fat milk is high in protein and calcium and low in calories. From non-fat dry milk you can make cottage cheese in only three minutes! You can also make pressed cheeses, sour cream, cream cheese, and yogurt.

HONEY

Honey is a natural sweetener, and it stores for a very long time. It is a healthier choice than sugar, which can suppress the immune system.

SALT

Salt is essential to any storage program because it enhances the flavor of food and provides necessary sodium in our diets. Most seasonings and soup bases use salt for flavoring. Salt is also an excellent preservative.

OIL

Polyunsaturated fatty acids are found in corn, soybean, safflower, and sunflower oils. Monounsaturated fatty acids are found mostly in olive, peanut, and canola oils. Most foods, however, contain a combination of all of the above. All oils are 100 percent fat and full of calories. Most oils are highly processed. The only oils we really need are those that occur naturally (in small amounts) in foods: fish, whole grains, and legumes. Natural fats occur in higher amounts in avocados, olives, nuts, and seeds, especially whole flax seeds. Olive oil is one of the best for storage. Oil is often overlooked in storage plans, but nothing contains more calories for its weight or space requirements. Shortening, butter, and margarine can be substituted for oil in most cases.

Wheat, "The Staff of Life"

by LeArta Moulton

"Bread is the staff of man's existence. Bread is wheat and wheat is earth, the good earth, the good black earth out of which comes man's food, his health, his vigor, his long life" (Louis Bromfield, author and horticulturist).

THE NEED FOR WHOLESOME FOODS

More and more, serious health problems are affecting people of every age group. What you eat and how you take charge of your body determine your fitness, health, and ability to fight diseases. You should start now to incorporate wheat and other grains into your daily meals to help build a strong immune system. However, your body needs to gradually adjust to this new diet and develop the enzymes it will need to handle the rich fibers contained in grains and legumes. Abruptly changing your diet from refined, processed foods to whole grains can be hard on your system. Introduce these foods to your system a little at a time.

KNOW YOUR WHEAT

The two general kinds of wheat are winter wheat and spring wheat. Farmers plant winter wheat in regions that have mild climates. Spring wheat is planted in regions that have extremely cold winter weather. Included in both winter and spring wheat are hard and soft varieties. Winter wheat is planted in the fall and harvested the following spring or summer. It starts growing before cold weather sets in, stops growing during the winter, then continues growing the following spring. On the other hand, spring wheat is planted in the spring and ripens during summer, usually a few weeks after the winter wheat ripens.

Choose hard winter wheat or hard spring wheat that is #2 Grade or better. Look for a high protein content—14 percent or higher. The wheat should be cleaned but not washed. The traditional hard red winter wheat is well known for its outstanding milling and baking qualities.

The new variety of hard white winter and spring wheat is very unique because it has protein and fiber levels comparable to high protein red wheat, yet produces a bread light in texture and color with a sweet taste. Many who are allergic to the red whole wheat are able to eat the white whole wheat.

High-protein wheat is best for making breads and gluten. It also stores better because of its low moisture content. Soft wheat can be used in many ways: sprouting, snacks, crackers, cereals, muffins, pastries, popped wheat, granola, and wheat chips.

NUTRITIONAL VALUE OF WHEAT

The wheat kernel's nutrient-rich bran and germ layers are loaded with antioxidants, healthful fatty acids, other minerals and phytochemicals (plant-based nutrients), in addition to the fiber. The nutrients in whole wheat are pantothenic acid, folic acid, biotin, choline, inositol, and vitamins B1, B2, B6, and E. The minerals found in wheat are iron, cobalt, potassium, magnesium, zinc, copper, and molybdenum. Vitamin C is not present unless the grain is sprouted. The protein content varies from 7 to 19 percent. In order to retain all these nutrients, the whole wheat should be used as soon as possible after grinding. If it is not used within ten hours it should be refrigerated. Hard winter wheat kernels contain at least 26 vitamins and minerals. Wheat kernels have three main divisions: bran, starch endosperm, and the inner embryo or wheat germ. Many important nutrients are removed when the endosperm layer is separated. The bran layer makes up 14 percent of the wheat kernel. This portion is removed when producing white flour. It is high in B vitamins. These vitamins serve your nervous system. The bran is also packed with other important nutrients, such as vitamins A, C, and E, plus calcium, iron, fluorine, and iodine. Wheat bran also happens to be one of the best sources of dietary fiber. High fiber diets aid digestion and help ward off disease. Like the bran, wheat germ contains high amounts of vitamins and protein. The germ is an excellent source of vitamin E, which is important to the skin's resilience and suppleness.

Nearly all the vitamins are milled out of wheat to make white flour, and only B1, B2, and niacin are added back in to make "enriched flour." Nearly 90 percent of the nutritional value is removed to produce white flour. Use freshly ground wheat to ensure high nutrition, protein, and fiber for extra energy and health.

Soft wheat, although low in protein, is still very beneficial for health. Use this wheat for sprouting and for making cracked wheat cereal, popped wheat snacks, and drinks, and any recipe calling for flour, (i.e. pastries, cookies, pie crusts, pasta, crackers, tortilla shells). Soft wheat is not ideal for isolating the gluten because the yield is not high. Nor does soft wheat make good light bread. You can add commercial gluten flour, or you can combine your soft wheat with legumes, which improves the amino acid balance dramatically and makes the proteins in both more easily assimilated. The ratio should be three parts wheat to one part legume. If you have to survive on wheat and legumes, you should sprout them as much as possible. Sprouting increases the vitamin and mineral content.

Vitamin E found in wheat slows down the aging process. It contains anticlotting factor, lowers cholesterol, increases blood flow to the heart, strengthens capillary walls, adds to fertility and male potency, protects lungs, and maintains muscles and nerves. The absence or shortage of vitamin E can cause tendencies to arthritis, cancer, heart disease, and cerebral hemorrhage. It is necessary for normal reproduction and lactation. Lack of this vitamin can cause miscarriage. It is necessary for growth. It helps build up the body to resist cancer and other degenerative diseases.

Vitamin B found in wheat increases your ability to learn and remember. It also builds up your resistance to disease and promotes a healthy heart, good digestion, and strong nerves. It aids normal reproduction and increases a mother's ability to nurse. It improves blood circulation, which strengthens skin, hair, eyes, ears, and liver.

Use of wheat's whole grain is important in building a digestive tolerance for roughage. If grains and legumes have not been a major part of your diet, start slowly by including small amounts each day of flour or cracked variations.

FACTS ABOUT WHEAT

Wheat is in the grass family and belongs to the group of grains called cereals. The wheat kernels, or seeds, are ground into flour to make bread and other products. These wheat products are the main food of hundreds of millions of people throughout the world. As a result, wheat covers more of the earth's cultivated surface than any other food crop. The wheat farmers of the world grow enough wheat every year to fill a freight train stretching one and a third times around the globe. Active wheat breeding in worldwide research programs continuously seeks for higher yields and enhanced nutritional content. For example, tritacale is a hybrid of rye and wheat, which makes it high in protein but without wheat's gluten-forming properties. Other research programs seek to produce wheat with higher lysine contents. The average amount of wheat used by each person in the United States each year is 118 pounds.

MILLING WHEAT

Many excellent home grain mills are available. You would be best served to purchase an electric mill with steel blades, which will enable you to grind all small types of grains and beans, even soybeans. Select a good hand mill for emergencies, for cracking grains, and for making cereals.

Storing and Preserving Wheat

Wheat can be stored in food-grade plastic, tin, or glass containers. The most common are #10 containers (approximately 13 cups or 9/10ths of a gallon) and buckets. Buckets lined with metallized plastic are the best. Your wheat should be stored in a cool, dry place. Avoid storing metal containers on cement or dirt floors. Set containers on wooden slats or shelves to prevent condensation and moisture from entering. Containers should be clean, free of odors, and able to be tightly sealed. Inserting oxygen absorbers is the most common method of keeping wheat safe. If you are unable to use these packets or to purchase products with oxygen absorbers, then a natural method is using packets of "diatomaceous earth."

LeArta Moulton is the author of *The Gluten Book*; *The Amazing Wheat Book*; *Quick Wholesome Foods* (video); and *Nature's Medicine Chest*.

WHEAT INSIGHTS AND TIPS

Cooked Wheat Cereal

There are many ways to cook wheat cereal. Here is one you may not know about. Use a thermos bottle to cook your wheat. First, heat the thermos by pouring in boiling water and letting it stand for about five minutes. Pour the water out, then add equal amounts of boiling water and washed (to get the dust off) whole kernel wheat (or any other grain) to the warmed thermos. Secure the lid and let stand for at least 8-10 hours. The kernels will be full and tender.

Cracked Wheat and Creamy Wheat Cereal

Cracked wheat and creamy wheat cereal can be made on the stovetop. Cracked wheat is the wheat kernel that has been very coarsely ground. The trick to cooking it so that it has a non-mushy, chewy texture is to first sift out any flour particles by using a fine wire strainer. The following quick method of cooking cracked wheat can also be used with other grains:

- Combine 1 cup of cracked wheat with 1½ cups of water in a saucepan. Bring to a full boil for 30 seconds. Cover the saucepan. Turn off the heat and let it steep for 15 minutes.
- To make creamy wheat, mix 1 cup of germade (the residue that has been sifted from the cracked wheat) with 1 cup of cool water. Boil 1 cup of water. Add the boiling water to the germade/cool-water mix and cook on a low boil until thick (about 1 minute). Add salt and honey for taste.

Versatile Rice

by Peggy Layton

Brown rice is the whole grain rice. Brown rice has greater nutritional value than white rice. Cooked brown rice has a nut-like flavor and is chewy. It retains its natural brown color and its natural coating of bran.

STORING RICE

Brown rice doesn't store as long as white rice because the outer shell of the hull contains oil that easily goes rancid. The shelf life of brown rice is about six months. To extend its shelf life, brown rice should be kept in the freezer. Once a container of brown rice is opened it should be kept in a refrigerator or in a cool place.

You should consider storing white rice in bulk. It is very versatile and a staple food for 70 percent of the world's population. The entire outer coating of bran is removed from white or polished rice.

PREPARING RICE

Some brands of rice have been enriched with vitamins and minerals that were lost in the milling process. For this reason you should not rinse white rice before cooking.

There are many varieties of white rice. These include short, medium, and long grain, basmati, parboiled, precooked or instant, processed, and wild rice. Rice products include rice flour, rice bran, rice noodles, rice cereal, rice oil, rice vinegar, and rice wine. Long grain white rice is one of the most versatile grains. It is easy to digest and children tend to enjoy its taste over other grains. For great flavors, rice can be cooked in beef or chicken bouillon or even fruit juices. Rice can be cooked with a vegetable juice cocktail, and it tastes delicious with reconstituted tomato powder. A variety of other food items such as reconstituted sliced mushrooms, onions, peas, and other vegetables, or bacon bits, slivered almonds, and herbs can be added to cooked rice to add variety and flavor.

Here are a few hints for cooking rice. Stick to the recipe and do not use too much water, which can result in soggy rice. Using too little water makes dry rice. Do not lift the pan lid when cooking rice. Lifting the lid lets out steam and lowers the temperature. Do not stir rice after it comes to a boil; this breaks up the grains and makes the rice gummy. When the rice is finished cooking, let it sit for a few minutes then transfer it to a bowl or another pan so it doesn't become packed down and clump together.

Another easy way to cook rice, especially brown rice, is to combine one cup of washed rice with two cups of boiling water in an oven-proof dish or pan. Cover and bake in a 350-degree oven for one hour. This can be an excellent meat substitute, especially if you use a black or wild Japanese rice (Japonica). It will have not only the texture of meat but the color as well.

Rice is a good meal extender. It contains protein, carbohydrates, calcium, phosphorus, and potassium, and it is low in fat.

Peggy D. Layton is the coauthor of *Cookin' with Home Storage* and the author of *The Emergency Food Storage and Survival Handbook; Cookin' with Rice and Beans; Cookin' with Powdered Milk,* and *Cookin' with Dried Eggs.*

The Nutritional Advantages of Beans

by Rita Bingham

Beans are low in fat and cholesterol-free, containing only 2 to 3 percent fat. They can even help lower cholesterol levels and are one of the richest sources of soluble fiber. Most beans contain at least 20 percent protein and are high in carbohydrates, which provide long-lasting energy. In addition, beans provide essential B vitamins and iron. Adding beans to your daily meals ensures total nutrition. Dr. Lendon Smith says, "When combined with nuts, seeds, or grains, beans form a complete high-fiber vegetable protein. A three-ounce steak will provide 350 calories and only about 15 grams of usable protein. One and one-fourth cups of cooked beans will provide the same number of calories and yet deliver 50 percent more usable protein." He goes on to say that when you grind dry beans into flour and add them to the wheat flour in all your baked goods, you create a perfect protein. Here are some insights into beans and tips about how to use them.

NUTRITION

Beans are high in fiber. Best of all, they are very low in fat, which means you can eat more delicious meals without having to count as many calories. Most bean varieties contain only 2 to 3 percent fat. By using beans that have been ground to a flour (small white navy beans work best) to thicken gravies and sauces, you increase the nutritional value of your meals, and your recipes will be virtually fat-free.

STORING BEANS

Store up to 125 pounds of assorted beans, peas, and lentils per person for a year's supply. The amount can vary depending on how many fruits and vegetables you store. The Benson Institute at Brigham Young University suggests that people require approximately one pound of fruits or vegetables (including beans) per day.

Both beans and grains have a protective, full-of-fiber outer shell. Once that shell is broken, nutrients decrease and deterioration begins. Fresh flours should be used within 1–2 weeks, or they should be refrigerated. (Flours should be placed in sealed freezer bags or wide-mouth quart jars and frozen.) Ideally, flours should be ground just before using, but that is not always possible.

USING BEANS

Super nutrition can be added to any commercial dry mix (cakes, cookies, muffins, breads) by adding a few tablespoons of bean flour to the dry ingredients, then adding extra liquid as necessary. If you desire to limit or eliminate meat from your diet, combining bean and wheat flours will provide you all the necessary amino acids to form a complete protein.

SOAKING

Dry beans, whole peas, and split peas (unless used in soup) need to be soaked before cooking. Lentils do not.

- Overnight Soak Method: wash and sort beans; place in large saucepan with six cups of water per pound of beans. Let stand overnight, then drain off soaking water and rinse well.
- Quick-Soak Method: follow the same washing and sorting instructions, but bring beans and water to a boil and cook for two minutes. Remove from heat, cover, and let stand one hour. Drain off excess soaking water. Add additional water and cook until tender.

Any bean, pea, or lentil, ground to a fine flour in the same way that you grind wheat into flour, makes an excellent "instant" creamy soup base. Simply combine bean flour, water, and bouillon and cook for three minutes. Then you can add pasta, vegetables, or even more beans for quick, healthy, homemade soup. When you make breads or rolls, substitute 1/4 of the required flour with finely ground bean flour.

MAKE YOUR OWN 3-MINUTE "CREAM OF CHICKEN" SOUP

Three-Minute Cream of Chicken Soup with Beans

2½ cups boiling water
1 tablespoon chicken bouillon or soup mix
½ cup finely ground white bean flour, mixed
½ cup cool water
1 cup diced chicken pieces (optional)

In a bowl, mix bean flour and water until smooth. In a saucepan over medium heat, whisk bean flour mixture into boiling water and flavoring. Stir and cook three minutes. Blend one minute for a "souper" creamy texture. Add chicken, if desired.

Serves 2 to 3. (For vegetarians, use vegetable bouillon or chicken-flavored soup mix in place of chicken bouillon.)

This soup can be used as gravy that not only tastes good, but also is good for you because it is practically fat-free. If you prefer milk, you can exchange 1½ cups of the required water with milk, or you can add about ¼ cup of evaporated milk to the cooked soup. Great for gravy or cream sauce.

This soup is also excellent with pasta or with as much as 1½ cups cooked potatoes, carrots, onions, celery, etc. Use one cup more water (4 cups total) and cook veggies until tender, then whisk in bean flour and cook two minutes after soup thickens.

QUICK BEAN GRAVY

Your leftover bean soups (made with light-colored beans) make a delicious gravy or sauce. Blend leftovers in your mixer and additional bean flour and bouillon as needed to thicken and to add flavor. Serve over potatoes, patties, loaves, biscuits, etc.

Beans for Protein

Beans are a versatile, low-fat source of protein that can be used to make any of the following: chili, 3-bean salad, burritos, Mexi-pita sandwiches, and even carrot cake. Believe it or not, beans taste delicious! Use them whole, pureed, chopped, or ground into flour to make health-promoting cakes, breads, and cookies. Beans can be added to hundreds of foods to enhance texture and nutrition and to improve your health and save money on your grocery bill. When you prepare meat dishes (such as tacos, burritos, casseroles, or stroganoff), try substituting 1 part chopped cooked beans to 1 part ground hamburger or turkey. Cook both together to allow the beans to absorb the juices and seasonings. Your family will never know.

Textured Vegetable Protein from the Remarkable Soybean

Textured vegetable protein is made from soybeans. The oil is removed from the bean before it is ground into flour. After the flour is formed into the desired texture or size, it is flavored to become any number of imitation meat products, including bacon bits, meat granules, or even large pieces of sausage or chicken. Textured vegetable protein is a meat substitute that is used in a variety of foods. When cooked, it resembles ground beef or chicken. Most people have eaten textured vegetable protein! It is used to make or enrich vegetarian burgers, hot dogs, chicken patties, ground beef (hamburger), chili, stew, sausage, and lunch meat. Many "bacon bits" that you use on salads and potatoes are actually made of textured vegetable protein. And textured vegetable protein is used by most convenience and fast foods outlets as a meat extender. Just check the label. If it says "texturized soy flour," then you know that the food contains textured vegetable protein.

There are many benefits to using textured vegetable protein in place of meat.

- inexpensive
- no animal fat
- a good source of protein and fiber
- long shelf life, convenient, and quick to use
- a good source of iron
- extends meat
- easier to digest than regular meats.

TEXTURED VEGETABLE PROTEIN AS A MEAT SUBSTITUTE

After textured vegetable protein has been hydrated, it can be added to any recipe that calls for meat. You can also use it as a meat extender. For example, if your recipe calls for 3 pounds of meat and you have only two, you can add textured vegetable protein to make up the difference. Sausage-flavored textured vegetable protein is very good in quiche and casseroles. You can also add it to gravy and pour it over biscuits or put it on top of pizza. Taco-flavored textured vegetable protein is great for burritos and tacos. You can make lasagna and all kinds of casseroles with the beef- and chicken-flavored textured vegetable protein. The possibilities are endless. Add the sausage-flavored textured vegetable protein to your scrambled eggs in the morning. Make a chip dip out of the taco-flavored textured vegetable protein by adding cheese sauce, salsa, and sour cream. Add the beef-flavored textured vegetable protein to spaghetti sauce.

Even the cheapest cuts of meat are more expensive than textured vegetable protein. Savings can be as much as 86 percent.

Textured vegetable protein is easy to prepare—even easier than real meat. When preparing ground beef you must thaw, fry, and drain it. With textured vegetable protein, just simmer in water for ten minutes and it is fully hydrated. Keep in mind that textured vegetable protein should be handled just as you would raw meat: make sure that your cooking area is clean and that you refrigerate the unused portion when it has been hydrated.

Rita Bingham is the author of *Country Beans; Natural Meals in Minutes; 1-2-3 Smoothies; Food Combining—the Natural Way*, and is the coauthor with Esther Dickey of *The New Passport to Survival*.

Dehydrated Milk

by Peggy Layton

Dairy products are very important in a food storage program. The best way to store milk is in dehydrated form. Dehydrated milk is high in calcium and vitamins. There are two types of dehydrated milk: instant nonfat and regular dehydrated milk. Instant nonfat powered milk is the best for storage.

Dehydrated milk can be used in any recipe that calls for fluid milk. Once reconstituted, dehydrated milk can be used in the same way and in the same quantity as fluid milk. The only difference between fluid milk and nonfat dehydrated milk is that nonfat dehydrated milk has had the water and the fat reduced. The nutrients remain the same; but dehydrated milk contains fewer calories and less cholesterol.

Most dried dairy products can be stored up to five years in properly sealed, airtight containers. Once a dehydrated milk container is opened, the milk needs to be used within six months to a year. You should also transfer the dehydrated milk into smaller containers, such as Snapware®, Tupperware®, or glass jars with lids. If the milk is exposed to moisture in the air, it will clump together upon reconstitution and make lumpy milk.

Use a mixer pitcher, wire whisk, or blender to blend the milk. It is best to chill the milk overnight before drinking it. Always store reconstituted dehydrated milk in the refrigerator just as you would store fresh milk. Some people mix it half-and-half with fresh milk.

When dehydrated milk is being used to make baked items such as cakes and breads, it can first be sifted into the dry ingredients and then the water can be added. Dehydrated milk can be used to make cheese, cottage cheese, yogurt, buttermilk, sweetened condensed milk, evaporated milk, whipped topping, ice cream, and sherbet. Dried dairy products that are available for long-term storage include cheddar cheese powder, buttermilk powder, margarine powder, sour cream powder, and butter powder.

Honey

by Peggy Layton

That delicious substance that bees make from the nectar of blossoms is a miracle of nature. Honey is a natural unrefined sweetener. It contains the natural minerals that are destroyed in other types of sugar when they are processed. Nutritionally, honey is better for you than most sweeteners, and it is typically easily digested. **However, children under the age of one should not be fed honey because they can contract botulism.** In the human body, honey does not need to be broken down into simpler sugars as do cane and beet sugars. Rather, honey is assimilated into the blood stream immediately, making it a good, natural alternative to refined sugar. Honey is sweeter and heavier than sugar; one cup of honey weighs approximately 12 ounces, while a cup of sugar weighs approximately 7 ounces. Therefore, you don't need to use as much honey when converting recipes that call for sugar.

Some of the different types of honey are raw honey, liquid honey, honeycomb, and crystallized honey.

To store honey, place it in plastic buckets or glass jars with lids. Honey does not crystallize if stored in a warm room (about 75 degrees F.). If you store it in an area that is below 55 degrees F., honey will become solid. To liquefy it, simply place the container of honey in a bowl of warm water until the crystals melt. Or, you can set honey in warm direct sunlight.

If honey is in a metal can, you should consider transferring it into glass jars with lids. Metal cans often rust over time, and rust affects the quality of honey. To produce honey that tastes good, producers frequently mix several kinds of honey together. The resulting flavor mirrors the flowers of blossoms from which the bees gathered the nectar. If your stored honey is old and has a strong flavor, you can add ¼ teaspoon of baking soda per cup of honey to neutralize the acidity. This makes for a more pleasing flavor.

Without having to change ingredients in a recipe, you can use honey to replace up to half the required sugar. Breads that are sweetened with honey should not be frozen because frozen honey deteriorates and the bread becomes mushy when it is thawed.

For hard cookies, substitute no more than one-third of the required sugar with honey. For more moist cookies, substitute no more than two-thirds of the required sugar with honey. Honey makes cookies softer than does sugar, plus some cookies will fall apart.

To substitute honey for sugar in cakes, cookies, or breads, follow this general rule: if the recipe calls for 1 cup of granulated sugar, substitute with ¾ cup of honey, then reduce the overall required liquid by ¼ cup. If you cannot reduce the liquid, add 4 tablespoons of white flour and ¼ teaspoon of baking soda. Bake at a slightly lower temperature (lower by approximately 25 degrees F.).

Cakes made with honey will retain moisture longer than cakes made with sugar. Honey-made products do not dry out or become stale as fast as sugar-made products.

Honey is truly an amazing miracle of nature and can play an important part in your food storage program.

HONEY INSIGHTS AND TIPS

HONEY, AN ANTIOXIDANT AND A SOURCE OF ENERGY

Antioxidants control free radicals in your body, which are believed to cause disease. Honey contains several antioxidants. Pinocembrin is found in honey. Additionally, honey can give you more energy. It contains a natural combination of glucose and fructose, which can prevent fatigue and enhance physical performance.

HONEY FACTS

- Honey contains more nutrients than refined sugar.
- The darker the honey the more minerals it contains.
- Honey should not be given to children under one year of age. It may contain bacteria that can cause infant botulism. Adults and children older than one year are typically not affected.
- Bees are the only insect to make food that humans consume. The worker bee will make only 1/12 teaspoon of honey in its lifetime.

Other Basics

OIL

Your food storage plan should include cooking oil. Vegetable oil (olive oil is best) and peanut butter can be easily stored to provide the necessary 5 to 10 percent of calories that we should get from fats. The American diet typically consists of more than 40 percent fat, far more than is necessary. During World War II, one of the most coveted items was vegetable oil. With a bottle of oil, one could acquire almost any other item. A quart could be traded for three bushels of apples or three hundred pounds of potatoes. Vegetable oil is high in calories and easily transported, and it makes foods taste better. Even wild flowers, wild plants, and roots can be cooked in vegetable oil and taste great. (For more information, see the "Oil" section under "Basic Foods and Better Health" near the beginning of this chapter, p. 32.)

SALT

Table salt is composed of sodium and chloride. One teaspoon of salt contains two grams (2,000 mg) of sodium. Sodium is a vital nutrient, playing an important role in maintaining blood volume and pressure by attracting and holding water in the blood vessels. Salt is needed by the body for enzyme reactions and to help balance acids and bases in the body. It also helps in the absorption of other nutrients, including carbohydrates. However, a little sodium goes a long way. Most Americans eat two to four times more sodium than they need. But if the kidneys are functioning properly, excess sodium should be excreted. A safe and adequate intake is about 1.1 to 3.3 grams of sodium daily. Again, one teaspoon of salt equals two grams of sodium.

GARDENING

Growing a garden is a wise investment, not only for the food but for developing food-growing skills. Even if your garden is small, the benefit can be great. Think of all the places where weeds grow. You can use these same places to grow nutritious vegetables or herbs for your family. Take advantage of every available bit of land or space to which you have access. Fresh fruits and vegetables will become the treats that you look forward to eating. Note: buy seeds that are packaged for long-term storage. Learn which vegetables grow well in your climate. Learn how to enrich your soil to produce more full and tasty foods.

Sprouting—Short-Term Food Storage

by LeArta Moulton and Rita Bingham

Sprouts are one of the most likely items that we may neglect in our diets. A good supply of sprouting seeds and water could become two of the most important items in your food storage.

Seeds produce sprouts. One of the best foods to eat is sprouts. Sprouts are living plant foods that are biogenic (life-generating), which means they transfer their vital life energy to you! They are packed with enzymes. Enzymes are crucial to digestion.

Most people eat much of their food after the food is cooked. Enzymes begin to die at 118 degrees F. and are completely destroyed at 130 degrees F. Therefore, *all* cooked foods lack these essential enzymes. When the body isn't *fed* enzymes, it cannot *make* enzymes. Indigestion is one of the first things to happen. Cooking food destroys the very enzymes that are needed so that food can be broken down and become small enough to pass through minute pores in the intestines and enter into the blood stream. When such foods are not digested properly their nutrients become essentially nonexistent and are eliminated as waste.

Then what happens? The body loses its ability to repair itself; imbalances take place, and the body begins to break down. The immune system is weakened. The body becomes susceptible to degenerative diseases, including cancer and arthritis. Whole, raw foods that contain complete enzymes are healthful and may help prevent illnesses. You should add fresh raw fruits, vegetables, and sprouts to your daily diet. Be sure to eat them *raw!* Wendy Campbell, a registered nurse and nutrition specialist, says, "They need to be raw because enzymes are only found in raw foods. Enzymes act as catalysts for the 10,000 functions per second that the cells themselves undergo. They strengthen the immune system, defy aging, and detoxify the body. Cooking (118–130 degrees) destroys the life quality of enzymes. Meat is cooked, milks and juices are pasteurized, grains are baked, and nuts are roasted. Fruits and vegetables are about the only other sources of enzymes, and even then we cook most of them."

Sprouts can be grown in your kitchen (from beans, lentils, grains, and other seeds) in any season. They provide fresh organic produce when no other garden is available. They are easy to grow—some in as little as one day. Seeds for sprouting can be stored for long periods of time and can produce many times their weight in fresh produce that is full of vitamins, minerals, and complete proteins.

In some schools of thought, it is said that life could be sustained if a person were to eat daily 1½ cups of a mixture of several different types of sprouting seeds. This mix would consist of equal parts Alaskan green peas, lentils, mung beans, and Adzuki beans, with half as much sunflower, fenugreek seed, triticale and regular wheat, plus a combination of alfalfa (allowed to green up a little), red clover, cabbage, and radish. These sprouts can also be eaten alone, in salads, with grains, in sandwiches, gently steamed with veggies, and as snacks, or sprinkled over soup. Everyone should store sprouting seeds and use sprouts in their daily diets. Sprouts are the best way to eat soy and an ideal way to eat all types of legumes. They are much easier to digest and cook in half the time.

During an emergency you could be faced with many concerns such as finding alternative cooking methods and preserving perishable foods. Sprouts can sustain you! Don't wait until an emergency has occurred, start now to introduce sprouts into your diet. They may be a food you need to get used to, but you will learn to enjoy their taste, and you will experience more energy and a feeling of well being.

TOOLS FOR SPROUTING
(any of the following):
1. A quart jar and a piece of nylon or wire mesh
2. Wash cloth, plate, and cake pan
3. Commercial sprouting trays

INSTRUCTIONS FOR PREPARATION
To experience a simple sprout recipe, try lentils. Soak 1/3 cup green lentils overnight (preferably in purified water) in a 1-quart jar, or purchase special sprouting jars with drainage lids. You can also use a lid made of nylon or fiberglass mesh, fitted with an elastic band or the ring of the canning jar. In the morning, rinse the lentils well with fresh water, then pour off the water through the lid or mesh. Turn the jar on its side to spread the seeds, then, to continue draining, leave the jar tilted at a 45-degree angle in a dark, warm place. Rinse and drain the contents of the jar once or twice a day. Lentils take about a week to

yield sufficient size sprouts. Once sprouted, rinse and let dry out a little then store in the refrigerator in an appropriate container. They will keep for about a week. (Beans take longer to sprout, so they need more rinsing. In two to three days the sprouts will be ready to eat.)

SUMMARIZING SPROUTING

- Sprouts are one of the most complete foods known to man, packed with vitamins, proteins, minerals, live enzymes, and fiber in their purest form.

- They are a whole food, nutritious, efficient, and the most inexpensive source of dietary fiber available.

- They taste good raw or cooked and have no waste. They are higher in protein than meat and higher in vitamin C than citrus fruits—at a fraction of the cost!

- Sprouts are easy to digest, and they add enzymes that change starches to sugars and proteins to amino acids.

- Bean and legume sprouts have a nicer texture than their adult counterparts; they can be easily chewed and digested, and require little or no cooking.

- Sprouted grains and beans are rich in vitamins A, B, C, E, and K. They contain greater amounts—up to thirteen times more—of riboflavin and folic acid over their adult counterparts. Vitamin C increases up to 600 percent in some cases. Two important amino acids, lysine and tryptophan, also increase significantly.

- They can grow anywhere, needing neither soil nor sunshine, flourishing in any climate during any season of the year, and they are ready to harvest in one to five days.

- Their yield is three to four times the amount of seed that you used for sprouting.

- Some of the easiest sprouts to grow are alfalfa, mung bean, chick pea, green or pink lentil, sesame, sunflower, almond, buckwheat, and wheat.

SPROUTING INSIGHTS AND TIPS

TEMPERATURES FOR SPROUTING

Never allow your seeds to become too hot or too dry. Temperature is the biggest killer of seeds. The latest research from Utah State University indicates that wheat that is in an oxygen-free environment will still sprout.

SPROUTS FOR VITAMIN C

How many sprouts would you have to eat to get a full day's supply of vitamin C? The general rule is ½ cup. Sprouts with leaves that are allowed to turn green have the highest level of *all* nutrients.

DEVELOPING A TOLERANCE FOR HIGH FIBER FOODS

Sprouting beans makes them easier to digest. However, each person will need to develop a tolerance to the high fiber content of beans, a process that can take several weeks if you were to use beans on a daily basis. Start slowly. Try using beans at one meal every day or two, but use only one or two tablespoons per serving. Mix into salads, soups, sandwich fillings, or casseroles. Your body has the natural ability to build up the intestinal flora to digest beans properly if you eat beans regularly.

Food Preservation Methods

FREEZE-DRIED FOODS

Foods processed in this manner are very popular because the food tastes very much like regular frozen food. Freeze-dried food is first "flash frozen" at extremely low temperatures in order to turn the food's moisture into tiny ice crystals. Next, low heat is applied in a vacuum chamber. The low heat melts the ice crystals without changing the food's existing cell structure. Finally, moisture is collected in the vacuum chamber, and the freeze-dried product is packaged for long-term storage. This process helps the product retain its color, texture, shape, flavor, and nutritional value better than other methods of drying. Freeze-dried foods can be quickly rehydrated, and they often require no cooking.

AIR-DRIED FOODS

Heat is applied at high levels for moisture removal. This process has been used for preserving food for millennia. By simply applying heat to certain foods, such as fruits and vegetables, dehydration occurs. This process typically takes more time than other methods of preparing food for storage, but it is very affordable. Air-drying is often called "the slow cook" process because it gradually removes moisture without totally cooking the product. Dehydrated fruits and vegetables make great snacks right out of the package, but all air-dried foods typically require 30 minutes in warm/hot water for rehydration. Be sure to store extra water for rehydrating freeze-dried and air-dried foods.

STORE-BOUGHT CANNED AND PACKAGED FOODS

These canned and boxed foods are, of course, what we eat every day. The processors of these foods concern themselves mostly with quality and taste, not with long-term storage. As a result, these foods typically don't have a shelf life beyond 8–12 months. When they are purchased at case-lot sales, they can be great values, and they are excellent for short-term preparedness. However, make sure you purchase them soon after the packaging date.

HOME-CANNED AND HOME-BOTTLED FOODS

Many families still put "sweat equity" into food storage programs. When you do it properly, this method can be very cost-effective. Home canning and bottling is an art that shouldn't be lost, and it's a lot easier than you may think. Home-canned products store up to 24 months depending on the food. To preserve as much nutrition and flavor as possible, you should store your food in the coolest, driest, darkest place in your home. However, for optimal freshness, usefulness, and enjoyment, we recommend ongoing rotation.

LOW-MOISTURE FRUITS AND MEATS

Low-moisture fruits and meats are considered "nature's candy." They provide an inexpensive and sweet alternative to sugary, store-bought foods. Fruit leathers and jerky are two other examples of snack replacements that you can produce at home for virtually pennies.

Dehydrated Foods

by Peggy Layton

Dehydrated food has had its moisture removed either through freeze-drying or air-drying. Dehydrated food is the next best thing to fresh food because the food has not been fully cooked. Dehydrated food retains many more vitamins and minerals than wet-packed canned foods. If properly sealed, dehydrated food stores well for long periods of time. Its shelf life is longer than wet-packed canned food. Whereas wet-packed food should be used within two years of canning, dehydrated food can last for five or more years.

Because the water has been removed, dehydrated food weighs less and stores in a smaller area than wet-packed food. It can be packed in #10 cans, plastic buckets, or other types of containers. We eat dehydrated foods every day. They fill the shelves of grocery stores. Many packaged convenience foods contain dehydrated ingredients. These include macaroni and cheese, oatmeal packets, hamburger and tuna pasta mixes, flavored rice mixes, instant soup, instant gravy, instant refried beans, biscuit mixes, cake mixes, hot chocolate, dehydrated milk, and almost anything that says, "just add water."

Packaged convenience foods contain dehydrated products such as dehydrated milk, eggs, sour cream powder, buttermilk, cheese blend, butter, margarine, and shortening. Soups and many main dishes contain freeze-dried or air-dried vegetables: cabbage, green beans, potatoes, carrots, peas, celery, broccoli, bell peppers, sweet corn, mushrooms, and tomatoes. Gravy mixes contain dried chicken, beef, and vegetable bouillon with dried mushrooms.

Think about all the things you purchase that contain dehydrated food. Macaroni and cheese contains dried cheese powder. Potatoes au gratin contains dried sliced potatoes and cheese sauce mix. Instant oatmeal packets contain dried rolled oats, dehydrated milk, dried fruit bits, and sometimes sweetened drink mix. Walk down the aisles of the grocery store and you will see dried fruit snacks such as banana slices, apples, apple bits, apricots, dates, figs, prunes, and raisins—all of which can be eaten dry or reconstituted with water, just like wet-pack foods.

Dehydrated dairy products include eggs, milk, butter, cheese, sour cream, and buttermilk. Keep in mind that butter powder, cheese powder, sour cream, and buttermilk taste differently when reconstituted, so it is best to use them for baking.

Don't be afraid to store freeze-dried or air-dried foods. You eat them all the time!

You Can Live on Soup and Bread

by Peggy Layton

I have a philosophy that you can live temporarily on soup and bread. They are staples. The pioneers always had a hearty pot of soup cooking on the stove. When the men would come home from working in the fields, they would have soup. The women prepared it every day. They used leftover vegetables and scraps of meat to add flavoring.

Dried soup mixes are available for us today. They can be purchased in bulk and will store for long periods of time. For that reason, they make ideal additions to a food storage program. If you have on hand a good variety of dried and commercially canned soups, you can use them to enhance the flavor of your basic storage items, such as grains, wheat, rice, lentils, dried green beans, peas, and pasta. Soup mixes can be used for gravies and sauces as well as being a great base for nutritious soup or stew.

Any of these soups will go well with a variety of breads, including yeast breads, white and whole wheat breads, fry breads, scones, bagels, pita and flat bread, tortillas, biscuits, rolls, pancakes, waffles, cakes, cookies, fruit pies, quick breads, muffins, and noodles.

The basic baking items that you need to have on hand include wheat and other grains for grinding into flour, white flour, dehydrated milk, dried whole egg, baking soda, baking powder, salt, and yeast. Sweeteners include white and brown sugar, powdered sugar, honey, molasses, and maple syrup. Fats include shortening and shortening powder, dehydrated butter powder, margarine powder, and oil (olive oil stores the longest and has the most nutrients). Spices include cocoa, cinnamon, nutmeg, vanilla, and powdered lemon juice. Other items that you may want to include are oatmeal, dried apples, dried bananas, and raisins. Nuts and chocolate chips are also possibilities, but they contain oil and won't store as long.

To calculate the amounts of each item that you will need to store, take your favorite recipes and determine how many people they serve and how many times you would make them—in one month, every three months, six months, and a year. You will discover that it is expensive to purchase a year's supply of all these items, but I suggest you start with a three-month supply. Proper planning will save you time and money.

Dried Eggs

by Peggy Layton

The best way to store eggs long-term is in dried form. Nutritionally, dried eggs are exactly the same as fresh eggs. Only the water has been removed. Dried eggs are high in protein and are available as 100 percent dried whole egg powder, which can be used as a substitute for fresh eggs, or in a dried scrambled egg mix, which contains mostly whole eggs with a little dehydrated milk and dried butter or shortening powder or dried egg whites. This egg mix makes light, fluffy omelets and scrambled eggs.

The recommended shelf life for dried eggs is five years if containers are kept cool and properly sealed. Once the containers are opened, the contents need to be transferred to glass quart jars with tight fitting lids and stored in the refrigerator. Then the eggs should be used within a year.

To reconstitute dried egg products just add water and stir with a fork. When a recipe calls for separating dry ingredients from wet ingredients, dried eggs can also be combined with other dry ingredients, and the water needed for reconstituting can be added to the wet ingredients. Dried egg products should not be used in any recipe that is uncooked or raw, such as eggnog, salad dressing, or ice cream. Bacteria can grow and cause salmonella poisoning.

In addition to scrambled eggs and omelets, many wonderful dishes can be made using dried eggs as the main ingredient—French toast, pancakes, waffles, quiches, soufflés, custards, and crepes.

DRIED EGGS INSIGHTS AND TIPS

Egg and dairy products can be combined with grains or legumes for protein-rich foods. Storing dehydrated milk and freeze-dried or air-dried cheese and eggs lends variety to your food storage. And the new dehydration technology makes these products taste great. Many people can't tell the difference between fresh dairy products and those that have been reconstituted. Because air-dried eggs taste so good and are so easy to work with, many restaurants use them in recipes. Storing dairy products is important for children who need calcium for their growing bones.

Following are two useful recipes that use dried eggs:

Dehydrated Hashbrown Casserole

5 cups water

2 cups dehydrated hashbrowns

1 teaspoon salt

2 tablespoons freeze-dried or air-dried onions

2 tablespoons butter or margarine

1 cup egg powder

1 tablespoon bacon bits (optional)

Grated cheese

Ketchup (for garnish)

In a 2-quart saucepan, add 4 cups water, hashbrowns, salt, and onions. Let simmer for 10–15 minutes until onions are hydrated. Drain well. In frying pan, melt butter or margarine. Add drained hashbrowns. Cook until browned and crisp (about 15 minutes). While hashbrowns are cooking, mix egg powder with 1 cup water. Blend until smooth (mixer pitcher or blender works well). Pour over browned potatoes and cook until egg mixture is set. (You may add bacon bits when adding egg mixture to hashbrowns.) Serves 6 people. May melt cheese over mixture and serve with ketchup.

The following recipe is great for emergencies, Scout campouts, and family outings.

Eggstremely Easy Omelet

2 tablespoons dehydrated scrambled egg mix

2 tablespoons water

Heavy-duty plastic freezer bag

Preferred seasonings such as salt and pepper

1 teaspoon cheese blend powder (optional)

1 teaspoon water (for cheese blend)

MRE ham slice (other MRE meat, freeze-dried meat, or meat substitute, such as reconstituted beef or sausage textured vegetable protein can be used instead)

Preferred garnishings such as onions, green peppers, etc. (Many freeze-dried or air-dried products can be used that you would normally use in an omelet, such as broccoli, bell peppers, freeze-dried meats, textured vegetable protein-flavored sausage, beef, bacon, ham, or chicken.)

Mix scrambled egg mix with water (equals 1 egg) in freezer bag. Add additional seasonings such as salt and pepper to taste. If desired add cheese blend powder and an equal amount of water. Seal plastic bag and mix by kneading bag until you achieve a smooth texture. Chop up part of MRE ham slice (whatever amount desired) and add to mixture. Add other ingredients for garnishing as desired. Mix, squeeze out air, and seal bag. Place the bag in boiling water for 3–5 minutes. Remove the bag from water when the omelet has reached desired consistency, and serve. For larger servings, add equal parts of egg mix and water.

Meals-Ready-to-Eat (MREs)

Originally designed for U.S. government use, Meals-Ready-to-Eat (MREs) contain delicious foods. These compact pouches have been used since the 1970s. A main concern in the development and testing of rations was shelf life. Now, all MRE foods are packaged in triple-layer plastic/aluminum. MRE pouches have proven to have better storage qualities than heavy cans. The MRE food is precooked and sealed at a high temperature so that bacteria are neutralized and the food will be stable when stored at room temperature.

Some of the best information available on MRE shelf life is listed on the chart below, which was compiled by the U.S. Army's Natick Research Laboratories.

TEMPERATURE AND STORAGE CHART

Storage Temperature(F)	Months of Storage
120°	1
110°	5
100°	22
90°	55
80°	76
70°	100
60°	130

Note: Below 60 degrees—not enough data yet collected. However, projections indicate that the 130-month storage life will be extended.

Also, time and temperature have a cumulative effect. For example, an MRE pouch stored at 100 degrees for 11 months and then removed to storage at 70 degrees would lose one-half of its 70 degrees storage life. Additionally, you should avoid storing MREs in areas that have fluctuating temperatures or in and out of freezing areas. A regular rotation of MREs of between five to seven years is recommended.

MORE ABOUT MRE SHELF LIFE

1. The shelf-life ratings shown in the chart were determined by taste panels—panels of "average" people, mostly office personnel at the U.S. Army's Natick Laboratory in Massachusetts. Their opinions were combined to determine when a particular component or the entire MRE ration was no longer acceptable.

2. The shelf life determinations were made solely on the basis of taste, since it was discovered that acceptable nutritional content and basic product safety would extend beyond the point of taste degradation. In other words, MREs would be safe and provide a high degree of food value long after the times suggested on the chart.

3. MRE pouches have been tested and redesigned according to standards that are much stricter than those used for commercial food. For example, the MREs must be able to endure abuse tests such as obstacle course traversal in field clothing; outdoor storage anywhere in the world; shipping under extremely rough conditions; 100 percent survival rating during parachute drops; 75 percent survival rating during free-fall drops; severe repetitive vibration; 7,920 individual pouch drops from 20 inches; and individual pouches being subject to a static load of 200 pounds for three minutes.

4. Freezing an MRE retort pouch does not destroy the food inside, but repeated freezing increases the chance that the stretching and stressing of the pouch will cause a break in a layer of the laminated pouch. These pouches are made to withstand 1,000 flexes, but repetitive freezing does increase the failure rate by a small fraction of a percent. Also, if MRE food is frozen, then thawed, it must be treated in the same way you would treat commercial food once it is thawed.

MREs FOR 72-HOUR KITS

MREs were originally designed for the military. They are some of the easiest and most nearly "normal" meals you can put in your 72-hour kit. They have an incredibly long shelf life—up to ten years (best if used within five years) when stored at temperatures below 60 degrees F. MREs also do not require cooking, water, or any preparation. They can be eaten cold. Main course entrees taste better warm and can be heated by placing the pouch in boiling water until it is warmed, or it can be set out in the sun. You can also purchase an MRE heater to use in place of a stove and cooking equipment. MRE heaters require only a small amount of water to activate them; no fuels, matches, or additional equipment needed.

Seven Major Mistakes in Food Storage

by Vicki Tate

"Considering conditions in the world," a woman told me, "my husband and I decided to put away some food storage. I bought twenty bags of wheat, some 60-pound cans of honey, and now all we have to do is get a couple of cases of dehydrated milk."

"Do you know how to cook with your wheat?" I asked.

"Oh," she chuckled, "if we ever need the storage, I'll learn how. Anyway, my kids only like white bread, and I don't have a wheat grinder."

She had just admitted every major misunderstanding about storing food (other than not storing anything at all). She's not alone.

ESSENTIALS

Here are seven important concepts to remember when planning your food storage program.

VARIETY

Many people only store the four basic items: wheat, milk, honey, and salt. Most of us could not survive on such a diet for several reasons: a) Some people are allergic to wheat and may not be aware of it until they eat wheat meal after meal; b) Wheat may be too harsh for young children. They may be able tolerate it in small amounts, but not as the

63

main staple in their diet; c) Appetite fatigue—we get tired of eating the same foods over and over. Young children and older people are particularly susceptible. The solution? Store wheat, become familiar with using it, and be sure to add other grains, particularly ones your family enjoys eating. Also store a variety of beans to add an array of color, texture, and flavor. Both whole grains and beans store well for long periods of time and are very inexpensive. Variety is a key to a successful food storage program. Store flavorings such as tomato, bouillon, cheese, and onion. Put away a good supply of the spices that you like to cook with. Flavorings and spices allow you to do many creative things with your grains and beans. Without them you are severely limited in the dishes you can create. Buy a good food storage cookbook, read it, and decide what your family really would eat. Notice the ingredients. This will help you know what to store.

EXTENDED STAPLES

Never put all your eggs in one basket. Store dehydrated and/or freeze-dried foods as well as home-canned or store-bought canned goods. Make sure you add cooking oil, shortening, baking powder, soda, yeast, and powdered eggs. You can't cook even the most basic recipes without these items. Strive for a well-balanced storage program.

VITAMINS

Vitamins are especially important if you have children, since children may not be able to store reserves of nutrients in their bodies as well as adults can. Most vital to your storage program are a good multivitamin, minerals, and vitamin C.

"QUICK-AND-EASY" AND "PSYCHOLOGICAL FOODS"

"Quick-and-easy" foods can help you through the times when you may be under too much stress to cope with preparing food, such as times of illness or in situations when you cannot safely make a fire. "No cook" foods such as freeze-dried foods are wonderful since they require almost no preparation. Other Quick-and-easy foods are MREs (Meals Ready to Eat) and canned foods, such as chili and soup. "Psychological Foods" are goodies such as Jell-O®, pudding, and hard candy. These may seem frivolous, but they can raise your spirit.

Balance

Too many people make the mistake of buying all their wheat, then buying all of another food storage item. Keep balance in mind as you build your storage. Buy a variety of items rather than a large quantity of one. If you suddenly needed to live on your present storage, you would fare better having a three-months' supply of a variety of items rather than a year's supply of two or three things.

Containers

Always store your bulk foods in food-grade storage containers. So often food is thrown away because it was susceptible to excessive sunlight, moisture, insects, or rodents. Use a food-grade plastic liner or metallized plastic bags—never use garbage bags—to line your plastic buckets. An excellent container is a #10 tin can, which is commonly used to store dehydrated foods.

Use Your Storage

Not knowing what to do with food storage is one of the biggest problems. It is vital that you and your family become familiar with the things you are storing. Learn to prepare these foods. This is not a skill that you will want to acquire during a time of stress. A stressful situation is the worst time to dramatically change your diet. Get a good food storage cookbook now. Learn how to prepare these foods and begin eating them!

FOOD STORAGE INSIGHTS AND TIPS

GETTING STARTED

If you have a limited budget, here are some things you can do that may cost you little or even nothing.

- Set aside a plot of land to grow some of your own food. For example, tomatoes don't take up much room. If you live in an apartment where gardens are not allowed, make a deal with a friend who has some idle ground in his or her yard or someone who owns a vacant lot. Share part of your crop. You can also grow plants in pots in a windowsill.

- Limit the amount of money you spend for expensive fast foods and for dining out. With the savings, purchase wheat, honey, and the basics. Within a short time, you and your family will be on your way to completing your food storage plan.

- Sprouting seeds cost pennies yet yield big dividends in quantity and nutrition. Sprouts make tasty additions to salads, sandwiches, soups, and stir-fry recipes. Sprouts are your fresh greens while you are waiting for your garden to mature.

- Cut down on waste. Plan a menu and stick to it. Buy in bulk. The extra is storage! Make sure you store extra or bulk items properly to avoid expensive waste.

- Budget a comfortable amount of money each week to use for your family's preparedness and food storage plan. You'll be amazed how fast your reserves grow.

- Can excess fruits and vegetables from your neighbors' unwanted crops.

Dr. Deloy Hendricks of Utah State University observed, "When I first started research in food storage, I asked Dr. D. K. Salunkhe 'What are the three most important considerations in food storage?' He responded, 'Temperature, temperature, temperature.' Thirty-five years of research has born that out. If you want to maintain food storage, keep it cool. Oxygen absorber packets can reduce oxidative rancidity and other changes, but they cannot prevent deterioration caused by high storage temperatures."

ABOUT NUTRIENTS

Most foods are combinations of minerals, carbohydrates, proteins, lipids (or fats), vitamins, and water. Since the individual nutrients in a given food deplete at varying rates, it is important to store (and eat) a variety of foods. Minerals and carbohydrates change very little in stored foods. If you store a food primarily for its mineral and carbohydrate content, you will experience very little nutrition loss over time. Proteins, however, are another story. For example, old wheat flour will not rise because the proteins needed to form gluten have been destroyed. Fats undergo enzymatic changes and become rancid and give off odors. The higher the fat content, the shorter the shelf life of the product. Vitamins are susceptible to destruction by heat, light, and oxidation. However, some foods contain high levels of particular vitamins and are still potent even after some loss due to age. A good rule of thumb is to store and eat a variety of foods, keep them as cool as possible, and become knowledgeable about your storage. (Special thanks to Utah State University Extension for these ideas.)

PROTEINS

Wheat, beans, and rice are considered "basic" foods because they combine to form a complete protein. Soybeans are complete by themselves. Vegetable proteins are more readily digestible and easier for our bodies to utilize. The Benson Institute suggests that 10 to 20 percent of our calories should come from protein foods. Some of the easiest to store sources of protein are fortified dehydrated milk, tuna fish, and beans.

WHEAT ALLERGIES

All recipes calling for whole or cracked wheat, including breads that require baking powder or soda as a leavening agent, can be altered. Use rice flour or other grain flours in place of wheat flour. Health food stores usually carry alternative, gluten-free flours. Spelt is a great substitute. Sprouted wheat seldom causes allergies.

OATMEAL

Besides being high in fiber, oats are rich in the nutrient silicon that nourishes the brain for clarity of thinking and helps calm nerves. It also benefits the hair, skin, and digestive system. The body needs to maintain a proper acid/alkaline balance. Tissues need to be alkaline. When they tip toward acidity, disease develops. Silicon is an alkaline-forming nutrient, and thus oatmeal is great for the system.

GRAINS AND LEGUMES ARE ESSENTIAL

A high percentage of your caloric intake should come from grains and grain products, and legumes (beans), peas, and lentils. Most of those grains and legumes should be whole grains, meaning whole, cracked, or ground into flour, but not processed. Ideally, your per-person year's supply would include 300 to 400 pounds of grain. Using and storing a variety of grains and legumes is essential.

COMPRESSED HIGH-ENERGY FOOD BARS

High calorie food bars (packaged for the Coast Guard) that are sealed for long-term storage contain a great deal of energy for their size and weight. They are nutritious and high in calories, making them a good choice for your 72-hour kit and preparedness plan. Compressed food bars are not as sensitive to extreme temperatures as are wet-packed foods.

PLAN AND STORE ALL FOOD GROUPS

Start with the foundation of grains. Don't forget fruits and vegetables. Incorporate foods that have protein, including dairy products. If you have stored only the very basics, you will be able to make only a few recipes. By adding even a few items—

grains, legumes, flavorings and spices—you greatly increase your options and the prospect of your family's surviving.

BREADS AND CEREALS

Breads, cereals, pasta, and rice are rich in complex carbohydrates (starches), which your body needs for energy. This fuel is so important that some nutritionists recommend that at least 50 percent of your daily caloric intake comes from complex carbohydrates. Think of breads and cereals as the coal that fuels the fire that keeps you functioning all day. By storing wheat, flour, and other grains, you have the basics of the bread and cereals group. Bread isn't the only thing you can make with stored grain. You can also make homemade pasta, soups, and more. You can even use wheat as a healthy and thrifty way to stretch your meat budget.

SPECIAL DIETARY NEEDS

If any of your family members has special dietary needs (due to diabetes, hypoglycemia, anemia, etc.), remember to include his or her special foods and medication.

INFANTS' NEEDS

If you have a nursing baby, you should pack formula in case you are unable to nurse because of shock or stress. Include both powdered formula and liquid formula in the event water is not available to mix the powdered formula. Include baby food for a toddler. Instant cereal, fruits, and vegetables are good choices. Remember to store extra water to reconstitute these items and update your 72-hour kit as your baby grows. According to information obtained from the Brigham Young University's agronomy department, beans mixed with grains form a high-quality, complete protein that can be tolerated by people of all ages, even infants, should breast milk not be available. For baby cereal, mix 1/4 cup very fine millet flour or brown rice flour with 2 tablespoons very fine bean flour (any kind) and 1 cup water. Increase to 2 cups water for formula.

OTHER CONSIDERATIONS

Can Opener

Be sure you have a heavy-duty, manually operated can opener for your food storage cans.

#10 Cans

How old is too old? There are many opinions on the subject, and there are many factors that determine how long you can practically store your #10 cans of food. The four most critical factors are moisture, oxygen, temperature, and food category.

Moisture

Generally, the higher the moisture content in the product, the shorter its life. Moisture allows bacteria and mold to grow, causing food to turn rancid more quickly. Moisture breaks down food.

Oxygen

This bountiful element is the key ingredient in oxidation—a process that adversely changes the chemical properties of food. To preserve food, oxygen must be taken out of it. Airtight containers help, but very few are 100 percent effective. The best solution is to use a small, safe, chemical-filled packet called an oxygen absorber, which, when used correctly, will remove up to 99.5 percent of oxygen from storage containers.

Temperature

Remember, when storing food, the higher the temperature, the shorter the life of the product. Store your food in the driest, darkest, coolest place possible.

USING YOUR STORAGE

Having food storage is one thing, but for many people using it is quite another.

- Do you know how to grind wheat and beans into flour?
- Do you know how much textured vegetable protein to use as a substitute for meat?
- Do you know how to incorporate dehydrated vegetables into your favorite recipes?
- Do you know when to use whole egg mix as opposed to scrambled egg mix in your cooking?

You don't want to wait until an emergency arises to learn how to use your food storage. Rotation is the key to a successful food storage program. There are several reasons you should rotate your food storage:

- To prevent food spoiling
- To minimize deterioration of the food's nutritional value
- To make the most of your money
- To minimize stress in an already difficult emergency situation
- To avoid surprising your family with a new menu in the wake of an emergency

USE YOUR STORAGE

Too many people end up throwing away most of their food storage. It becomes rancid. They are too hesitant to use their food storage. "The food tastes bad; I don't know what to make; it is too time-consuming to use food storage." ROTATE your food storage. Acquiring delicious, budget friendly food storage items needn't be difficult. Do you know that only TEN items in your storage could create up to 50 meals? Add three more items and you can make 75. Five more items can make it possible to create hundreds of delicious, nutritious, inexpensive meals. A common misconception is that food storage will last forever. All foods are subject to deterioration as time passes. Chemical changes occur, causing foods to change texture, color, and taste, and lose vitamins and proteins. Rotating your food will ensure optimum freshness, taste, and nutritional value.

SAVE MONEY

When you regularly use your food storage, you suddenly have an economical and practical way to shop for groceries. Buying in bulk is less expensive than purchasing in smaller quantities. Instead of buying a 5-pound bag of sugar, pay a little more and get the 25-pound bag—it is much cheaper per pound. Buy wheat instead of flour. Wheat is substantially less expensive, takes up less space, and it will store up to ten times longer. Shop case-lot sales and stock up on the foods your family enjoys.

EVERYDAY USE OF YOUR STORAGE

By using a combination of dehydrated butter and shortening, and dehydrated and/or freeze-dried vegetables and fruits, and even textured vegetable protein as a substitute for meat, your emergency or camping meals can be extraordinary, and you can leave your cooler at home when camping.

INVENTORY

Keep paper and pencil available to record storage items that you add and remove. You will be able to see immediately what items you need to replenish.

BOTULISM

While extremely rare, botulism is the worst problem you can encounter in home-bottled or canned wet-pack goods. Never use foods from containers that are leaking or bulging. Avoid using food from badly dented cans, cracked jars, or jars that have loose or bulging lids. Do not consume food that has a foul odor. Discard any container that spurts out liquid when you open it. Don't even taste such food!

FREEZER FAILURE

Don't panic if your freezer temporarily fails. Freezers are well insulated, and each package of frozen food acts as a block of ice, protecting the food around it. Ordinarily, a fully stocked freezer will keep food frozen for two days after losing power. A half-full freezer can keep food frozen for about one day. Don't continue to open the door to check on the temperature level; you will let the cold air escape.

POWER OR REFRIGERATOR FAILURE

Try not to open the refrigerator door too often. Depending on the warmth of your kitchen, your food should stay cool from four to six hours. For longer outage or repair periods, you can place block ice in your refrigerator to keep it cool. Also, dry ice can be added to the freezer compartment.

INCREASING STORAGE LIFE

To keep your foods fresh as long as possible, store food in a cool place in food-grade containers that can be tightly sealed to keep oxygen and moisture at minimal levels. If your home doesn't have a basement, store containers under your bed, on the floor of a dark closet, or in the lowest of your cupboards—always away from heat sources such as furnace vents, hot water pipes, or kitchen oven. Avoid storing food in an attic, garage, high cupboards, or outdoor sheds, or close to a source of heat. NEVER store food items or water next to gasoline, kerosene, chemicals, or cleaning products. Do not store containers directly on a cement floor. Place containers on boards, pallets, or metal racks.

EASY STORAGE GOAL

Obtaining a two-weeks' supply of food is a good goal to work toward if you feel a year's supply is impossible. Even if you live in an apartment, you can usually find room to store two weeks' food. Starting small puts the task within reach. Store away a little extra each week and before you know it you will have reached your goal!

FOOD STORAGE CALCULATOR

Type the following website link in the address box of your Internet browser, then hit ENTER or click on GO. It is a good resource to help calculate your basic storage needs.

http://www.providentliving.org/emergencyprep/calculator

CHAPTER FIVE

WARMTH, SHELTER, AND CLOTHING

Staying Warm

by J. Allan South

Few discomforts are more annoying and potentially dangerous than being cold. Hunting expeditions that have been "overstayed," sudden storms, failed vehicles, outdoor activities, and other circumstances can cause an emergency situation. Every year many people die of hypothermia. It doesn't necessarily need to be extremely cold to induce hypothermia. Many fatalities occur in at forty or fifty degrees. Why? People become wet and cold; then they panic and do something unwise such as removing their coats. A review of how we stay warm and what can happen when we don't, emergency shelters, clothing, and lightweight winter emergency kits are important for preparation.

HOW WE STAY WARM

We stay warm through generating and retaining heat and/or gaining it from an outside source. Heat is lost through radiation, conduction, convection, and evaporation.

RADIATION

The effect of radiation may be felt by putting your hand close to a hot stove. The heat radiates out from the heat source. Our bodies radiate heat, and this process can be reduced through the use of insulation.

Most thick outer garments, such as heavy coats or layers of lighter-weight clothing minimize radiation loss.

Radiant barriers constructed of shiny material sandwiched with nonconductive layers reflect body heat *inward*. These "emergency blankets" are very effective considering their thickness and weight, and they are recommended for any emergency kit. The best ones are those that are shaped like a sleeping bag, since they prevent air currents from stealing heat. Also, these "cocoons" do not allow moisture to escape, an important consideration.

CONDUCTION

Conduction is another way heat is transferred away from its source. An example is when one end of a nail is heated and the heat gradually moves to the other end. Conduction is prevented by separating the two extremes with an insulative layer. Most coats, natural and synthetic, offer resistance to conduction through air pockets in the insulation, which prevents heat from moving away from the body. Since water is about twenty-five times more heat-conductive than air, wet insulating materials conduct heat more rapidly than dry materials.

CONVECTION

Convection transfers heat via air currents. We experience convection when we leave our jacket unzipped, allowing the heated air from our body to escape through the opening.

EVAPORATION

Heat loss occurs when water evaporates. Our bodies continually give off moisture—or "sweat." If we become damp with perspiration or with water from another source, evaporation removes precious calories from our bodies.

To safeguard against evaporative heat loss, avoid becoming wet from an outside source and limit perspiration. In an emergency situation, try not to work so hard that you make yourself sweat. Take off layers of clothing; work more slowly; put on a raincoat; do whatever it takes to prevent becoming wet, either from the outside or inside your clothing. Wearing undergarments that wick the moisture away from the body is very helpful.

STARTING A FIRE

Starting a fire can help both physically and emotionally. Carry some "strike-anywhere" or "wind-proof" matches. Other fire-starting sources are high-intensity butane lighters or flint and steel (with magnesium is best). Some form of flammable material such as pellets, pastes, or fine steel wool can be helpful. Another source of flammable material is cotton impregnated with petroleum jelly and stuffed into a 35mm film canister. Try it; it works great!

Here are some other useful tips. Light a stout candle to give you a long-lasting flame for starting your fire. Place flammable tinder on a small sheet of aluminum foil that will act as a dry, reflective bed for starting a fire. Remember to take a small, lightweight, fold-up saw or a hatchet. A knife is indispensable in any emergency kit.

Here is some advice for the novice fire builder: You will need lots of fine, dry tinder. Never try starting a fire without gathering several times the amount you estimate as minimal.

EMERGENCY SHELTERS

In an emergency situation, finding shelter is important. Shelter provides protection from wind, water, and perhaps cold temperatures. A tube tent, a tarp made of coated fabric, polyethylene sheeting, or a poncho can be used to keep out water and block deadly wind. Cord or nylon rope—always part of an emergency kit—can be used to erect and support the shelter. For example, you can stretch the cord between two trees, and secure one end of a tarp over the cord. Then stake or hold down the other end with rocks or other heavy objects. Or you can drape a tarp over a branch or log, and similarly secure the ends to the ground. Still another method is to use a pole in teepee fashion and secure the edges.

Of course, a "real" tent is a great option, but in an emergency situation one may not be available. Emergency gear is usually confined to very lightweight items. Native American tepees are wonderful shelters, as are canvas military- or sheepherder-style tents. Nylon and other synthetic tents dominate the market because they are inexpensive, light-weight, and full of interesting design features. The popular large nylon tents are either dome-shaped with a rain fly, or they are made with a canvas roof. A nylon tent should have a waterproof fly that covers the tent as much as possible on all sides. Most small, inexpensive tents are made for warm weather and provide liberal ventilation. A four-season tent is constructed so that the ventilation panels can be closed. Always anchor your tent. Winds can come up quickly and can ruin tents or scatter equipment. Never put a tent away wet. Moisture will promote the growth of mold and ruin the fabric.

If you need to find shelter in a natural setting, look for recesses under ledges, the area under branches of large fallen trees, thickets, and the area at the base and under the branches of a large standing tree. However, in an electrical storm, such trees are more likely to be struck by lightning.

A lean-to of branches and boughs will give significant protection from wind and wet weather. And of course snow caves are possibilities if the construction material is available. Snow caves give considerable protection from wind and extreme temperatures; however, you should never make a snow cave where there is danger of avalanche.

The location of a shelter is an important consideration. Choose a place that provides some protection from the wind. Keep in mind that wind generally blows down canyons in the evening and up the canyons in the morning. Also, more wind blows at the top of a ridge or at the bottom of a canyon than somewhere in between. Always consider the possibility of flash floods and avoid making your shelter in gullies or low places.

CLOTHING AND BEDDING

Some general rules for surviving cold weather are as follows:

DRESS IN LAYERS

Wear undergarments made of polypropylene or polyester next to the skin. They are very good at wicking moisture away from the body. Cotton is one of the worst materials for extremely cold conditions. Cotton holds in moisture and, when it becomes wet, conducts heat away from the body. Clothing made of wool is better because it has some ability to insulate when it becomes wet. However, it does not wick as well as synthetic materials do. Wool functions better when it is worn away from the skin.

The next layer should be comfortable clothing made of fleece or other insulative synthetic or wool. Finally, add a coat or shell and additional pants if needed. Down-filled garments are great as long as they remain dry, but when wet, the down clumps together and loses its insulating ability. Synthetic materials, on the other hand, are very effective and most provide some insulation when they become wet. The warmth factor for this layer of clothing is largely dependent on the amount of "dead air space" it provides between your body and the material.

These guidelines for insulation and thickness also apply for the head and neck. There is an old but true saying: "If you want to keep your feet warm put on your hat." The head and neck areas are major sources of heat loss. Always make sure they are protected. Knit watch caps, fleece hats with earflaps, Peruvian-style hats, wool hats, and synthetic-insulated hats all work. Spend five bucks or fifty. Look goofy or great. But carry a hat. A synthetic or wool scarf is also effective in keeping the neck and face warm.

The outside layer should be a well-designed, wind-proof, water-resistant (or waterproof) shell with an integral hood. The hood should provide variable closure around the face and neck, and it should have a drawstring at the waist to control airflow. If the shell hangs below the waist (which is best), it should also have a drawstring at the bottom. It should open and close so that heat can be captured or released to avoid perspiration. If the shell is not made of Gore-Tex® or a similar fabric, a poncho or raincoat is also recommended. Fabrics such as Gore-Tex® allow water vapor to escape through tiny holes or a tight matrix fiber, but water from the outside will not penetrate it. However, in extremely cold conditions, body moisture can freeze to the inside of the fabric, effectively turning the garment into an icebox. Depending on the temperature, layers of clothing can be added or removed to control warmth.

Another important type of cold-weather clothing is open-cell foam. Properly made, open-cell foam clothing of an appropriate thickness has no peer for both keeping you warm and controlling the accumulation of moisture. Open-cell foam is better than any commonly used synthetic or down, and it can keep you warm hour after hour, day after day. The problems are: 1) it doesn't drape well; 2) it is a little bulky; 3) it is hard to find in prefabricated clothing, and when it is found, it is a little pricey. Do-it-yourself construction is possible and greatly reduces the cost. In an emergency involving cold weather and a vehicle, remember that the seat cushion has the best insulation available. Cut the seats open, stuff the foam inside your clothing, and use the insulation as a head covering.

WEAR THE RIGHT KIND OF SHOES AND SOCKS

Sturdy shoes are priceless. In cold conditions rubber-bottom boots with layers of wool felt, synthetic insulation (or some combination of the two), or foam work well. Foam insulation is warmer but may be harder to walk in. Aim for a good comfortable fit, and be sure you know about the shoes' ability to keep your feet dry. Good wool or wool/synthetic socks are essential. Gaiters prevent snow from getting inside shoes, or a cheap alternative is to duct-tape pants to boots so that moisture cannot enter. No cotton socks!

HAVE ADEQUATE SLEEPING BAGS

As with other gear, design and construction of sleeping bags determine their usefulness. Sleeping bags are filled with down or synthetic materials, as are coats. The outer shells and linings are made of synthetics or cotton. Some bags have an outer shell of Gore-Tex® or a similar fabric, which adds greatly to their cost. A few bags also include a shiny, reflective, breathable layer in the insulation. Sleeping bag shapes vary but are basically either rectangular, with or without a hood, or mummy-like. The mummy style provides less room and weighs less. Some people feel claustrophobic in a mummy bag, but otherwise these bags are great. In any case, the bag should be long enough to cover the head, or it should have a hood that can be closed with a drawstring. A mummy bag should also have a collar that can be closed around the shoulders.

Down is absolutely the finest filling for sleeping bags if it can be kept dry. It is comfortable, lightweight, and compresses easily. However, a synthetic bag of comparable quality is usually less expensive, heavier, and less compressible. But it may keep you just as warm. When a synthetic bag becomes wet it is superior to a wet, down-filled bag.

A sleeping bag should be compressed in a stuff sack as infrequently as possible. Compressing wears out insulation fibers and gives them "unconstructive memories," whereby they lose their capacity for loft and for insulating dead air spaces. Store sleeping bags in large, breathable bags; then hang them or lay them loose in a storage area.

An insulating ground pad is necessary for maintaining warmth when you are sleeping on the ground. A closed-cell, full-length pad is inexpensive and will provide essential protection. More expensive models add comfort, but a pad is a must.

LIGHTWEIGHT WINTER EMERGENCY KIT

A lightweight winter emergency kit should provide for food and water, shelter, signaling, safety, sanitation, and some way to kindle a fire. Consider some or all of the following components:

WATER AND FOOD CHECKLIST
- ❑ Container of water (at least 32 ounces)
- ❑ Stainless steel cup or pot

- ❑ Water filter or purification tablets
- ❑ Granola or energy bars, nuts, dried fruit, trail mix, jerky, bouillon, energy drink mixes, MREs, emergency rations

SHELTER CHECKLIST

- ❑ Poncho, tube tent, and/or a seven- or eight-foot square of lightweight tarp made of coated fabric or plastic
- ❑ Ground pad, or at least a two-foot square piece of a ground pad to sit or lie on
- ❑ Emergency blanket or bag
- ❑ Cord or lightweight rope (twenty or thirty feet)
- ❑ Duct tape
- ❑ Wool blanket

SIGNALING ITEMS CHECKLIST

- ❑ Whistle (louder and easier than trying to yell)
- ❑ Signal mirror
- ❑ Flare (optional)
- ❑ Orange marking tape (to leave your mark)

SAFETY AND SANITATION ITEMS CHECKLIST

- ❑ First aid kit
- ❑ Sunglasses
- ❑ Compass
- ❑ Light (flashlight, headlamp, light stick, extra batteries)
- ❑ Small plastic shovel (garden shovel type is adequate)
- ❑ Toilet paper and/or paper towels in a plastic sack
- ❑ Hand sanitizer

FIRE-STARTING MATERIALS CHECKLIST

- ❑ Strike-anywhere or windproof matches in a waterproof container
- ❑ Lighter (high-intensity butane lighter preferred)
- ❑ Flint and steel
- ❑ Tinder, fuel, candle, sheets of aluminum foil
- ❑ Saw or hatchet
- ❑ Steel wool and 9-volt battery
- ❑ Magnifying glass

J. Allen South is the author of *The Sense of Survival*.

WARMTH, SHELTER, AND CLOTHING INSIGHTS AND TIPS

HEATING AND COOKING

- **Camp stove.** A quality camp stove with fuel can be a source of warmth as well as a cooking aid. Most camp stoves are lightweight and easy to use. You may want to purchase one that uses multiple fuels—kerosene, unleaded gas, alcohol, aviation fuel, etc.

- **Emergency stoves.** Staying warm is important, especially if there is an emergency during winter months. Emergency stoves can be used. Make sure you allow for sufficient ventilation because the fumes from gas stoves can kill you.

- **Stove safety.** Never use a stove in or near your tent. Never open fuel containers on or near a hot stove. Never try to refuel a stove that is hot. Carry a small maintenance kit for your stove for repairs.

- **Kerosene and oil lamps and lanterns.** These light sources are great decorations, and they are also very useful in an emergency.

- **Open-pit fires.** Build fires in designated fire pits. If there are no designated fire pits but making a fire is permitted, locate an open area away from low branches and dry vegetation. Clear a ten-foot circle and make a fire pit of rocks, silt, clay, sand, or other nonflammable materials. A small pit, approximately 4 to 10 inches deep, is sufficient. Surround your pit with small rocks to add extra protection. Next, set up a cooking fly that faces away from the wind to provide protection from wind, rain, sleet, or snow. A cooking fly can be made of a tarp or a heavy, fire-resistant blanket. String it between two trees, poles, or sticks, and place it about ten feet from the fire.

- **Burning wood.** The harder the wood, the slower and cooler the wood will burn. The softer the wood, the faster and hotter the wood will burn.

- **Storing extra fuel.** Store extra fuel far away from your cooking area. At home, store fuel in approved containers and, if possible, store outside the house.

SHELTER

- **Camping trailer.** A camping trailer can double as a preparedness resource. In case of an emergency, make your trailer ready to use by stocking it with extra blankets, clothing, and other useful items.

- **Freestanding tents.** These are great for preparedness. They are easy to move once they have been set up, and you can set them up on sand, snow, or rocks. They are usually lightweight and they have fewer poles that can break. However, you should remember to stake them down in case of wind.

- **Tents with aluminum poles.** The poles are strong, light, and resistant to corrosion.

- **Tarps.** A tarp can make the difference during an emergency. Keep one on hand to put under your tent, to cover your food, or to hang up to protect your family from the wind and rain.

CLOTHING AND BEDDING

- **Packing logically.** Make sure you pack your backpack or 72-hour kit in a logical order. Smart packing will save you time in an emergency because your pack will be more organized when you need to use items.

- **Storing clothing.** Store only clean clothing and fabrics in a dark, dry, cool, bug- and dust-free environment. Use large plastic trash cans with lids, bins, boxes, suitcases, zippered garment bags, footlockers, chests of drawers, or cedar chests.

- **Dark-colored clothing.** Dark prints and plaids look nicer longer. They tend not to show dirt or wear as quickly as light-colored and solid-colored clothes.

- **Cleaning clothes.** Be sure to have a backup plan for cleaning your clothes. Products such as the Wonder Washer® are great for preparedness.

- **Durable sturdy shoes or backpacking boots.** These are great to have in your preparedness kit. Good protection and support for your feet are critical in an emergency, especially after an earthquake or tornado.

- **Sunglasses and sunscreen.** Other great protection items include sun block, insect repellent, lotion, and hand sanitizer. Wear sunscreen (at least 30 SPF) and protective clothing if you are going to be in the sun. Apply sunscreen 30 minutes before exposure. Sunscreens are labeled with an SPF (sun protection factor). The SPF is a multiplying factor. If you would normally be all right in the sun for 10 minutes, and if you are using at least 10 SPF sunscreen, you should be all right in the sun for 100 minutes. Find the sunscreen that will work best for you.

- **Sleeping bag liners.** A sleeping bag liner is great to put inside your sleeping bag to provide more warmth and to keep the interior of the bag clean.

- **Dry cleaning a sleeping bag.** Never dry-clean a down-filled sleeping bag. The solvents will destroy the feathers' natural oils, affecting their resiliency.

CHAPTER SIX

LIGHT, TOOLS, COMMUNICATION

Light

by Barry Crockett

When the power goes out, we are effectively plunged back into the first century A.D. Preparing alternate sources of light for use during emergencies is a must. The luxury of having electrical power during a disaster is not something you should count on. Light is especially vital in caring for children, the elderly, or those who may be ill, injured, or disabled. Since most of us have never had to rely upon nontraditional  forms of lighting, we may not be aware of other available options.

A fire built in your home fireplace or wood stove can provide useful light as well as heat, but wise planners will prepare in advance for other alternate light sources to meet the demands that often accompany short- or long-term disasters and emergencies. A combination of light sources is best to have on hand—both at home and in your emergency kit.

EMERGENCY LIGHT SOURCES

One of the safest emergency lights is the chemical light stick. These small lights are normally activated by bending the stick, which sets off a chemical reaction inside that causes the unit to glow. Since there is no spark involved, these provide an added measure of safety

when there is a chance of gas fumes being in the air.

Another form of emergency lighting is the candle. One of the safest and longest-burning candles is the 100-hour candle. Be sure, of course, that there is no chance of gas fumes before lighting. The most common is made of liquid paraffin. It is amazing how much light a small candle can produce and how effective it is in restoring a sense of comfort and tranquillity.

Innovation has helped us in the past few decades with regard to lighting. The hand-generated flashlight (often with a radio) is one example. These flashlights work after various methods of cranking have occurred. The dynamo cranking charges built-in batteries, which power the flashlight.

One of the latest innovations is the LED (light emitting diode) bulb. These bulbs generate an amazing amount of light without using much battery strength, and the bulbs can last for thousands of hours. The bulbs are shockproof and less fragile than common flashlight bulbs. Most LEDs use space-age, solid-state circuitry, which allows bulbs to last up to fourteen times longer than common flashlights. Other flash-light options are rechargeable, solar-powered, or magnetic-powered.

Waterproof, heavy-duty flashlights are good to have in your emer-gency kits and at home. Remember to always have extra batteries on hand.

When the emergency is such that you may not have electricity for a longer period of time, then you may want to have on hand kerosene lamps or propane lamps. Kerosene is the safer of the two fuels to store and generally recommended for a more permanent light source. These lamps come in a variety of styles, and are the lamps our grandparents used.

LIGHT INSIGHTS AND TIPS

CANDLES

Candles are one of the most reliable sources of light. All you need is a match. Wax candles are inexpensive and easy to store. You can also purchase liquid paraffin candles that last longer than wax candles. Liquid paraffin candles are smokeless and odorless and have an indefinite shelf life. Remember, the longer the wick the more light your candle will emit.

LIGHTING AREAS

Make sure you have an emergency light source in all major rooms in your house, such as the kitchen, hallways, family rooms, and bedrooms.

EXTRA BATTERIES

Extra batteries are essential. Some flashlights will drain the batteries of their power when left in the flashlight, even if the light is turned off. So do not make the mistake of counting on these batteries to work.

OTHER LIGHTING EXTRAS

Remember to store extra chimneys, wicks, mantles, matches, burners, fuses and other "replacement" parts that may be needed for your lanterns.

PRACTICE

Practice using your emergency lighting so you can move quickly and confidently in an emergency.

Tools

Most homeowners know the value of having the right tool at home when repairs are needed. A simple tool can make such a tremendous difference in an emergency. Following is a list of tools you may want to have available:

- ❏ Pocket knife/multi-purpose tool
- ❏ Shovel
- ❏ Hatchet or ax
- ❏ Sewing kit
- ❏ 50-foot nylon rope
- ❏ Can opener (non electric)
- ❏ Adjustable wrench for turning off gas valve
- ❏ Tool kit, including screwdriver, pliers, and a hammer
- ❏ Duct tape, plastic tape, staple gun, and plastic sheeting for temporary window replacement
- ❏ Work gloves
- ❏ Fire extinguisher
- ❏ Saw and pick
- ❏ Mattock (a useful digging and grubbing tool)
- ❏ Hoe

Communication—Your Key to Safety and Rescue

by Barry Crockett

In an emergency, you will need to be able to communicate for your family's safety. You will need to have contact with the outside world and receive current information from emergency authorities in your area. You will need to be able to communicate with medical professionals and other key people on whom your family members rely.

In times of developing emergencies, stay tuned to the radio or television and await instructions. If evacuation is recommended, you should move quickly but calmly and follow instructions (route to be used, evacuation shelter to be sought, etc.). Have access to several different means of communication. These will keep you informed and, if necessary, aid rescuers in locating you or a family member. Maintaining a flow of information helps to eliminate stress. Emergency broadcasts typically focus on disaster locations and how to avoid them. They will provide weather updates and information about the status of the emergency. They may also give you tips on how to remain safe. You should become familiar with the locations of emergency agencies such as the Red Cross.

METHODS OF COMMUNICATION

RADIOS

Radios are powered in a variety of ways—battery, solar, hand crank dynamo. They also receive many types of signals: AM, FM, TV, weather bands, and short-wave bands.

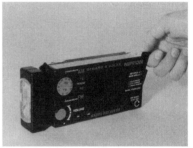

WALKIE-TALKIES/TWO-WAY RADIOS (FM TRANSCEIVER), CB (CITIZENS BAND)

These are often used in hiking, hunting, and search and rescue operations.

WHISTLE

A whistle can be heard much farther than can your voice. A whistle is a must for all emergency kits.

SIGNAL MIRROR

A signal mirror can be seen for miles under the right conditions.

PAPER AND PENCIL

Paper and pencil are important items for leaving messages and recording your thoughts.

MOBILE AND CELLULAR PHONES

In an emergency, cell phone systems easily overload. If you are using a cell phone, make a quick call to your contact person and ask him or her to relay messages for you.

COMMUNICATIONS INSIGHTS AND TIPS

MEETING PLACES

Have a back-up plan. Don't count on your cell phone to find family members. Plan to meet at a specific place outside the disaster area—church, school, or other prominent building. Also choose several alternative places to meet. Let the local Red Cross and other authorities know where you are and who you are looking for. They will provide the greatest assistance. Plan to meet back at home only when the emergency is over and you can safely return. Finally, choose a person who lives outside your local area whom all family members can call. Make sure all family members, including all children, memorize that person's phone number.

FAMILY COMMUNICATION

- Establish in advance who your out-of-area contact will be.
- Everyone should carry with them a card with the out-of-area contact's name, address, and day and evening phone numbers. Let your children's teachers know who your family's out-of-area contact is.
- At all times, each family member should carry a prepaid phone card or enough change to make several phone calls.

CHAPTER SEVEN

FIRST AID AND SANITATION

First Aid

YOUR RESPONSIBILITY TO KNOW

Throughout your life you may be faced with a variety of injuries. Whether it is a simple paper cut or a severe chemical burn, every accident must be dealt with in the right way. Your knowledge of first aid could mean the difference between life and death for a stranger or loved one. Your ability to take responsibility and make the best decision will depend on your working knowledge of first aid. Remember, your goal should be to provide effective help until qualified medical professionals arrive.

GETTING STARTED

Classes are usually offered through the American Red Cross, local hospitals, and local educational institutions. CPR and first aid certification are important for you to obtain, maintain, and renew. Classes are offered for all ages and skill levels and usually take only three to four hours to complete. You can learn how to assist in the delivery of a baby; set a broken limb; control bleeding; and help a person who is choking. You can learn how to protect yourself from infectious diseases and how to care for people of various ages. These classes will help as you establish a home library of first aid reference books and materials, some of which should be included in your 72-hour kit.

CREATING YOUR FIRST AID KIT

You can take much of the guesswork out of creating your first aid kit by purchasing a preassembled kit. Then add to your preassembled kit the items that meet your particular needs. Don't forget prescription medicines. Also be sure to include special items needed by small 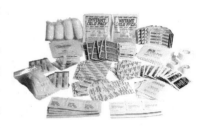 children or the elderly. Kits come in all sizes and range from containing only basic items to containing professional surgical kits. Determine what items you would need the most and how much of each item you would need. For example, families with small children would probably need extra bandages. You can adapt a first aid kit for a particular place or activity (e.g. auto kit, camping kit, home kit, business kit). Remember, you should purchase a kit that contains items that best meet your needs. A surgical kit is a valuable asset, but you would first need to gain necessary knowledge to use it correctly. Look over the list of basic first aid items below.

BASIC FIRST AID CHECKLIST CONSIDERATIONS

- ❏ Sterile dressings
- ❏ Splints (different sizes)
- ❏ Snakebite kit
- ❏ Emergency blanket/bag
- ❏ Mouth-to-mouth shield
- ❏ Adhesive tape closures
- ❏ Sting relief
- ❏ Antacid tablets
- ❏ Mole foam/moleskin
- ❏ Burn relief creams and pads
- ❏ Small flashlight and batteries
- ❏ Tongue depressors
- ❏ Specialized medications
- ❏ Children's pain relievers
- ❏ Kaopectate® and Ipecac® syrup
- ❏ Diarrhea medicine
- ❏ First aid book
- ❏ Eyewash
- ❏ Paper and pencil/pen
- ❏ EMT shears
- ❏ Protective glasses
- ❏ Calamine® lotion

- ❑ Petroleum jellies
- ❑ Adhesive bandages
- ❑ Extra large adhesive bandages
- ❑ Butterfly bandages
- ❑ Adhesive spot bandages
- ❑ Fingertip bandages
- ❑ Knuckle bandages
- ❑ Elastic bandages
- ❑ Burn bandages
- ❑ Burn gel
- ❑ Sterile pads
- ❑ Iodine prep pads
- ❑ Eye pads
- ❑ Sterile eye wash
- ❑ Alcohol preps
- ❑ Gauze and sponges
- ❑ Transpore tape
- ❑ Micropore tape
- ❑ Surgical tape
- ❑ Antiseptic towelettes
- ❑ Protective gloves
- ❑ Antiseptic ointment
- ❑ Ammonia inhalant
- ❑ Pain reliever
- ❑ Instant ice packs
- ❑ Safety pins
- ❑ First aid cream
- ❑ Bandage scissors
- ❑ Tweezers
- ❑ Appropriate bag/container
- ❑ Hemostats
- ❑ Scalpel
- ❑ ABD (abdominal) pads
- ❑ Triangular bandages
- ❑ Heat packs
- ❑ Personal prescriptions
- ❑ Thermometer
- ❑ Triple antibiotic cream
- ❑ Sterilized water packets
- ❑ Antibacterial soap

OTHER CONSIDERATIONS

Make sure you update and maintain your first aid kit often. Keep a good first aid book in your kit. Here are some other things to keep in mind:

- Adhesive bandages are great for dressing small wounds. Make sure the bandage is big enough to cover the wound. If it isn't, use a dressing instead. Be sure the sterile seal wrap is not broken.

- Sterile dressings are cloth pads that are placed directly on a wound to protect and control bleeding. They should be used when a wound is too large for a bandage.

- Eye pads are soft, sterile pads that are used to protect the eye when it is injured until medical attention can be obtained.

- Wearing protective gloves is always a good idea, especially if you are in contact with another person's blood or body fluids.

- Hemostats are used for stitching.

- ABD (abdominal) pads are large, absorbent, sterile pads used to stop bleeding from larger wounds.

- Burn relief supplies can reduce sharp pain and begin the process of healing.

- If you are backpacking or hiking, consider the following first aid supplies: fever reducing drugs (aspirin, acetaminophen), anti-inflammatory drugs (aspirin, ibuprofen), medication for diarrhea, medication for nausea, anti-itch medication (hydrocortisone cream), petroleum jelly and lip balm, medicated foot powder, talcum powder or corn starch, moleskin, hydrogel dressing (Spenco 2nd Skin®), nail clippers, sunscreen, sunburn relief medication, insect repellent, insect bite medication, and snake bite kit.

FIRST AID INSIGHTS AND TIPS

STORING FIRST AID KITS

Store your first aid kit in an easy-to-access, convenient part of your home or automobile. Also, you should keep a portable first aid kit in your 72-hour kit. To survive most emergencies, you must act quickly. The first aid items that you keep with your 72-hour kit should be in a compact, lightweight compartment such as a duffel bag, backpack, or carrying case. In any case, do not store your kits in a hard-to-reach place such as an attic or storage closet. A common mistake is to add too much to your first aid or 72-hour kit. Remember that your kits should be lightweight and easy to carry.

TREATING PUNCTURE WOUNDS

If possible, contact a medical professional. A puncture wound is usually caused by a sharp, pointed object such as a nail or needle. Puncture wounds can be serious. Germs can be pushed into the wound by the object. Puncture wounds are difficult to clean. If the object has penetrated the bone, it can abscess. This is especially risky if the sharp object has

gone through a tennis shoe. The foam in tennis shoes is known to harbor a type of bacteria called pseudomonas, which can cause infection. Flush the area thoroughly with water to clean well. Elevate the wound. Watch for signs of infection such as redness, swelling, persistent pain, pus, or fever. We repeat, contact a health professional. Wear a clean sock and shoe to protect the area while it is healing. Make sure your immunizations against tetanus (lockjaw) are current.

TREATING MAJOR WOUNDS

If possible, contact a medical professional. For severe bleeding, apply constant pressure—up to twenty minutes—to the wound with a sterile dressing, if available. If there is a foreign object in the wound (such as a glass shard), don't press directly, but apply pressure adjacent to the wound area. If broken bones or dislocations are suspected, do not move the affected limb. Immobilize by a splint, if possible. If you are certain there are no breaks, you can gently elevate and support the injured part while keeping pressure on it. This action should minimize bleeding. Dress the wound with sterile, nonsticking material as soon as possible and obtain professional help.

FIRST AID TIPS TO REMEMBER
- Remain as calm as possible.
- If possible, contact a health professional immediately. Step away when professionals arrive.

- Keep unnecessary people away.
- Check frequently for signs of infection.
- Never abandon the victim.
- Employ bystanders for relaying messages.
- Reassure the victim that you are there to help. Try to calm the person.
- Keep emergency phone numbers by each phone in your house.
- Review first aid procedures with family members on a regular basis.
- Keep first aid supplies well stocked and in accessible areas in your home, vehicle, and 72-hour kit.
- You can only help to the level of your knowledge and your access to available supplies. Take a first aid class and know how to use the supplies.

HOUSEHOLD POISONS

More than a million cases of poisoning are reported to poison control centers annually in the United States. Most often these cases involve children under the age of six. Children are very curious and like to taste and sample almost everything they see.

What is a poison? It is any substance that can cause serious harm to the body when inhaled, absorbed, or ingested. Household poisons come in four basic forms: solids, liquids, sprays, and fumes. Paints, plants, and prescription medicines are just a few of the many sources of potentially dangerous poisons. Here are some prevention and preparation tips:

- Don't store cleaning or similar solutions in food-type containers.
- Don't store or prepare food and chemical products in the same areas.
- Keep children away from areas that have recently been sprayed with insecticides or weed killers.

- Keep medications locked away and out of the reach of children.
- Teach children not to eat wild plants or mushrooms (they could be toadstools!) growing in the yard.
- Know how to contact your local poison control center.

WHAT TO DO IF YOU SUSPECT POISONING

You should already have written emergency numbers, such as the number to the local poison control center, by your phone. Most products are labeled with instructions for treating accidental poisoning. With some products you should induce vomiting, with other products you should avoid vomiting to prevent further injury. Some chemicals require an antidote, such as milk. Do not attempt to treat the person before first calling a medical professional for instructions. Poison control centers are open 24 hours a day, seven days a week. They dispense emergency information and, depending upon the situation, they may advise home treatment, or they may refer you to a hospital or doctor's office. They will ask you questions, which may include the following:

- What is the name of the product and its ingredients?
- What is the approximate quantity ingested and when did ingestion occur?
- What is the age and weight of the person exposed to the poison?
- What is your name and telephone number?

IMPORTANT BOOKS

Include an emergency preparedness or survival manual in your emergency kit. *The Boy Scout Field Book* is excellent. Other reading materials, paper, pencils, crafts, and games can help you focus on something besides the disaster at hand. Disaster victims often request a Bible. Keep a first aid kit and handbook in an accessible place in your automobile. You never know when the need may arise to assist someone.

VACCINES, TETANUS, AND IMMUNIZATIONS

Keep them up to date.

RED CROSS

To find your local chapter of the American Red Cross, simply go to the main website www.redcross.org and enter your zip code in the designated area. It is important to make sure the information you get comes from a credible source.

EMERGENCY PHONE NUMBERS

Having an emergency phone list by your phone brings peace of mind. Take time to list people and agencies that you would want to have available to you in the event of an emergency. Make your children aware of these numbers and regularly review possible situations in which you would need to use them. Use the form below as a starter. Write in important phone numbers. Check your local phone book for police and fire stations, poison control, Ask-a-Nurse, hospitals, and the American Red Cross.

EMERGENCY CONTACT NUMBERS

Any emergency: 9-1-1

Fire station:

Police station:

Family doctor:

Poison control:

Animal control:

American Red Cross:

Federal Emergency Management Agency:

School numbers:

Local friends or relatives:

Out-of-area contact (family member or friend):

Work numbers:

Neighbors:

Other important numbers:

Sanitation

MAKESHIFT TOILETS

Portable toilets are available that consist of a 5- or 6-gallon bucket equipped with a lid that looks and works like a normal toilet seat. Use a plastic garbage bag inside the bucket to collect refuse. You can purchase an enzyme product that is used in sewage treatment plants, septic tanks, cesspools, drains, and grease traps. It is noncaustic and noncorrosive.

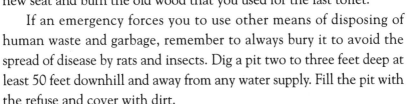

If you do not have a portable toilet, you can dig a latrine trench about four feet deep and 18 inches wide. Lay logs across the hole for a seat. After use, cover the waste with small amounts of dirt to decrease the odor. Remember that a covered toilet reduces odor more than an open toilet. You can make a toilet cover with wood or a large leaf. If the odor becomes oppressive, fill the latrine completely with dirt and dig a new one. Build a new seat and burn the old wood that you used for the last toilet.

If an emergency forces you to use other means of disposing of human waste and garbage, remember to always bury it to avoid the spread of disease by rats and insects. Dig a pit two to three feet deep at least 50 feet downhill and away from any water supply. Fill the pit with the refuse and cover with dirt.

PORTA-POTTY

During an emergency, sanitation systems could be down for days. Have a backup plan for convenience and to avoid disease. A "Porta-

Potty," a commercially made toilet, is an easy and quick solution. Have a good supply of bleach or other disinfectant. You may want a privacy curtain, and don't forget the toilet paper and other sanitation supplies.

KEEPING FOOD AND UTENSILS SANITARY

Keep all your "eatable" food covered and off the ground. After drinking or using water, cover containers. Do not wash dishes where you get your drinking water, and wash them where the water will not go into anyone's drinking supply. To prevent the spread of germs, use clean plates or eat out of the original food containers. Before eating fruits and vegetables, wash and peel them. If refrigeration is not available, prepare only as much as you will eat at a meal. Wash your eating utensils with purified (treated) water.

SANITATION CHECKLIST

Here are some suggestions for assembling and personalizing a sanitation kit:

- ❑ Plastic bucket with toilet seat lid
- ❑ Commercial sanitation kit
- ❑ Heavy-duty garbage bags with ties
- ❑ Deodorizer tablets/enzymes for reducing odor
- ❑ Soaps: personal antibacterial soap (bars last longest), laundry, and dish washing soap
- ❑ Toilet paper
- ❑ Moistened towelettes for washing yourself
- ❑ Baking soda (to use as toothpaste and deodorant and to treat heat or diaper rash)
- ❑ Shampoo and personal grooming supplies
- ❑ Towel and washcloth
- ❑ Infant needs (diapers, creams, wipes, powder)
- ❑ Toothpaste and extra toothbrushes
- ❑ Feminine hygiene products
- ❑ Razors, shaving cream, extra blades, shaving lotion

❑   Extra pair of protective gloves

CLEANLINESS

It is important to keep your body and hands clean. Avoid over-handling food. Keep your fingers out of your mouth. Pay attention to what you touch. In emergency situations, everything touched can carry disease. There will be less of a chance of your contracting or transmitting disease if you wash your hands, especially before handling food or drinking water, before and after caring for the sick, and after using the toilet.

WASHING CLOTHES

Wash or disinfect clothing as often as practical, especially underwear and socks. Disinfecting clothing, not necessarily laundering it, is the most important health objective in difficult shelter conditions. Dipping clothing into boiling water can disinfect it. Unless plenty of water is available for rinsing, do not disinfect clothing by placing it in a chlorine bleach solution.

PRIVACY SHELTER AND CAMP SHOWER

Privacy for sanitation purposes is a must in any preparedness plan. A privacy shelter can be used as a restroom with a portable toilet, a place to shower with a camp shower, or a place to change your clothes. Sanitation and cleanliness can revive and regenerate your body and spirit. When creating your preparedness plan, be sure to remember sanitation and sundry items, including a privacy shelter and camp shower.

CHAPTER EIGHT

DISASTER PREPAREDNESS

Emergency Education Quiz

How much do you know about emergency preparedness? In a crisis, would you panic or prevail? The answer may surprise you. Take this fun quiz to test your knowledge on various disasters and emergency preparedness. Answers are listed at the end of the quiz.

1. True or False? As long as a thunderstorm is at least five miles away from you, you are pretty safe from lightning strikes.

2. In an earthquake situation, you should:
   A. Run outside to avoid falling building debris.
   B. Take cover under a heavy piece of furniture.
   C. Panic.
   D. Lean against an inside wall or stand under an inside doorway.

3. What is the minimum amount of water that you need to store for one adult for two weeks?
   A. 5 gallons
   B. 10 gallons
   C. 14 gallons
   D. 21 gallons

4. Which areas of the United States are vulnerable to earthquakes?

A. The West Coast, particularly California

B. The Eastern seaboard

C. The central United States

D. All 50 states

5. What's the most common disaster that occurs in the United States?

A. Fire

B. Flood

C. Earthquake

D. Tornado

6. What's the number one, disaster-related killer in the United States?

A. Fire

B. Flood

C. Earthquake

D. Tornado

7. If your car stalls while you're trying to evacuate from a flood, you should:

A. Stay inside the car until assistance arrives.

B. Leave it.

C. Call a towing service.

D. Flag someone down to help you start it.

8. True or False? Small games and a teddy bear are important components for your 72-hour kit.

9. When treating frostbite, you should:

A. Rub the limbs down with snow.

B. Give the victim a hot cup of chocolate (caffeine) to warm up.

C. Gradually warm the body by wrapping in dry blankets.

D. Plunge the affected areas in hot water.

E. None of the above.

10. The most dangerous part of a hurricane is:

    A. Breaking waves.

    B. Gale-force winds.

    C. Flood-causing rains.

    D. Landslides.

11. How often should you practice your emergency evacuation plan?

    A. Once a year

    B. Every six months

    C. Every three months

    D. Am I supposed to practice my emergency evacuation plan?

12. Why are 72-hour kits called 72-hour kits?

    A. Most disasters are over in 72 hours or less.

    B. Three days is how long survival food lasts outside the home.

    C. You can't carry more than three days' worth of items at a time.

    D. It generally takes at least 72 hours for emergency personnel to reach you.

ANSWERS:

1. False. If you can hear thunder, you are in danger in a thunderstorm. Lightning can strike within 10 miles of the rain area. Just because the storm isn't right on top of you, doesn't mean you are safe. If you can, take cover in a building or vehicle.

2. Either (B) or (D). Find cover under something heavy, such as a sturdy desk or chair. Or you can use an inside wall or doorway. Just make sure to keep away from places where glass could shatter.

3. (C) Fourteen gallons is the minimum amount of water you should store for an adult. This amount allows an adult one gallon of water to use per day for fourteen days. Remember, however, in normal

conditions, the average adult uses about 100 gallons of water a day for drinking, cooking, bathing, and sanitation purposes. You may want to store more based on your individual and family needs.

4. (D) Even though earthquakes occur most frequently west of the Rocky Mountains, all 50 states and U.S. territories are at risk. Forty-one states and territories are at moderate to high risk.

5. (A) More homes will be threatened by fire than by any other disaster. This is one of the reasons a fire escape plan is crucial for every home. Flood is the second most common disaster.

6. (B) Floods, particularly flash floods, are the number one weather-related killers in the United States. Flash floods cause the deaths of nearly 200 people a year.

7. (B) Leave your car and move to higher ground. Many deaths have occurred when people have tried to move their stalled cars in a flood.

8. True. A few small games or a stuffed animal provide welcome comfort for both small children and adults.

9. (E) None of the above. Here is a note from nursing school: "Remove clothing from affected area very carefully. Do not rub a frost-bitten area. This can cause serious tissue damage. Immerse the affected part(s) in warm, NOT HOT, water, no warmer than 105 degrees F. If the temperature is uncomfortable for you, it's too warm. Avoid touching the body part to the side of the water container. Keep the frostbitten part(s) in the water until it looks red and feels warm. Pat dry gently and loosely bandage in dry, sterile dressings, placing cotton or gauze between fingers or toes. Do not break any blisters. Seek follow-up medical attention."

Remember, the body needs to warm up gradually. DO NOT give a frostbite victim coffee or any caffeine. As a stimulant, caffeine can speed up the heart and quicken the effect that cold has on the body.

10. (A) Even though many deaths and great destruction can be caused by wind, rain, and landslides, it is breaking waves, known as the storm surge, that causes the most damage. During a hurricane, this wall of water slams into the coastline, causing flash floods and structural damage to buildings.

11. (C) Your emergency evacuation plan should be practiced at least four times a year so your family is prepared.

12. (D) In a major crisis, it generally takes at least 72 hours for basic services to be up and running and for emergency personnel to reach you.

General Disaster Preparedness Information

RADIOS

Radios are helpful in monitoring the status of a disaster. The best models are those that are solar-powered or dynamo-powered (hand-cranked). If you use a radio that requires batteries, be sure to keep a fresh supply of batteries on hand. Check expiration dates on the batteries and rotate them regularly. Do not keep batteries inside the radio because they expire more quickly and may leak.

ELECTRICAL OUTAGE

- Check to see if your neighbors have power. If you are the only home without electricity, check the main fuse in your electric service panel or fuse box to see if the main circuit breaker has been tripped or if a fuse has blown. If you don't know how to check, consult a qualified electrician or call your power company.

- Report the outage to your power company.

- Close the windows and try to keep outside doors shut as much as possible to trap residual warmth inside the house. Put on more clothes or snuggle under some blankets.

- To reduce the possibility of damage due to electrical surges and to reduce the electrical demand once power has been restored, unplug computers, television, VCR/DVD players, microwave ovens, etc., and turn off all major nonessential appliances such as the electric range and the washer and dryer. Turn off the majority of household light switches.

Leave at least one on so that you will know when power has been restored. You may find that it becomes necessary to cut power to the entire house.

- Try to keep your refrigerator and freezer doors closed to conserve the cold air inside.
- Open the window shades to allow more light to come in.

THINGS TO HAVE ON HAND

- ❑ Battery-powered or hand-crank radio
- ❑ Wind-up clock
- ❑ Breaker fuses
- ❑ Portable heater and cooking stove
- ❑ Flashlights and fresh batteries
- ❑ Extra blankets and warm clothing

AUTO FIX-IT KIT

An auto fix-it kit should be a do-it-yourself mechanic's shop. Pack tools in a tough toolbox. Store the toolbox in your trunk for simple repairs to get you back on the road. (See Chapter Two)

WINTER CAR BREAKDOWN

If you break down, DO NOT leave your car. It is the best shelter you can have in a winter storm. If you have a cell phone, call for assistance. While you are stuck and if you are able to start the car, run the engine for about ten minutes every hour to use the heater. Make sure you crack a window on the side away from the wind to get fresh air. Periodically check to make sure your tail pipe is not blocked by snow or other objects. If you find an obstruction, to prevent carbon monoxide poisoning, you should clear it before engaging the engine.

ICE AND COLLISION PROBLEMS

Ice can freeze your vehicle doors shut or they could become jammed by collision. Therefore, as soon as severe weather warnings are issued, move selected emergency items inside the passenger compartment. Keep inside your car a hammer, Samurai survival tool, or a small pry bar to pry yourself free from a door jammed by a collision.

PREPARING YOUNG CHILDREN

Here are a few things to teach your young children:

- Teach them to dial 9–1–1, *not* "nine-eleven."
- Pictures and symbols can be used to identify certain emergency assistance numbers if the child is too young to read. For instance, the phone number for the fire department could be listed beneath a picture of a flame.
- Important emergency contact numbers to have handy include fire station, police station, family doctor, poison control, animal control, American Red Cross, school numbers, work numbers, local friends or relatives, and out-of-area friends or relatives.
- Help your child memorize important family information such as their address and phone number. If they are too young to memorize information they could carry a small index card that contains emergency information to give to an adult.
- If someone is supposed to pick your child up from school, teach your child a "secret password."

BEING PREPARED AT WORK AND SCHOOL

Emergency situations can happen anywhere. Keep emergency supplies in a desk drawer, locker, or another allowed space. This emergency kit could include the following:

- Flashlight with extra batteries

- Emergency blanket (very compact and made of a special material that reflects up to 80 percent of your body heat)
- Food (Meals Ready to Eat, high calorie food bars, jerky, granola bars, fruit bars, candy bars, crackers, fruit leather, raisins, nuts, trail mix, prepackaged foods)
- Water pouches or Aqua Blox®
- Pocket knife (may not be allowed)
- Hand and body warmers
- Lightweight plastic poncho
- Small first aid kit (plastic bandages, rolled bandages, pain reliever, essential medications, gauze, antiseptic spray, antibiotic cream)
- Reading material to relieve stress

Contact your school district to find out about their emergency plan and policies about how your children would be released from school in case of an emergency.

PROTECTING IMPORTANT DOCUMENTS

Most people do not organize their documents and instead have them scattered throughout their home. When an emergency occurs, there is not usually enough time to find vital documents. The following are items that you should consider protecting in a fireproof safe. In addition, all family members should know where medical records are kept.

- Will (You will probably need the original for it to be legally binding. Make several copies.)
- Trust documents
- Personal and family records
- Cherished photos and keepsakes
- Business files
- Collector items
- Legal and financial documents

- Family heirlooms
- Birth certificates
- Deeds
- Titles
- Cash (Checks and credit cards are typically ineffective during a major emergency.)
- Duplicate keys
- A record of bank and credit card account numbers and phone numbers
- Financial portfolios
- Copies of licenses (vehicle, professional, marriage, etc.)
- Inventory of valuable household items (include pictures)
- Family videos
- Jewelry
- Any other items that would be difficult to replace

It is a good idea to keep the originals in a safe, but keep additional certified copies outside the home in a safety deposit box or with relatives.

SIGNALING FOR HELP

Signals that indicate you need help come in threes. Signal from rescuers should be in twos. The following are universally recognized signals:

- Three fires in a triangle pattern. When using fire as a signal remember that bright fires are more easily seen at night, and smoky fires make a better signal in the day.
- Newspaper or aluminum foil (reflective-type emergency blankets also work well) weighted down with rocks to make a large triangle.
- Make letters that contrast with the ground color in a large clearing by using sticks, newspaper, or branches, or by stomping through the snow. These letters need to be at least

twelve feet tall and the width of each line needs to be two feet wide. "SOS" or "HELP" indicate a general need for help. An injury is indicated by the capital "I." An "X" means you are unable to proceed. An "F" indicates you need food and water.

- Use a mirror to reflect the sun. Groups of three flashes signal distress.
- Use a whistle. Make three unmistakable blasts. Pause for a few seconds between each blast, wait a couple of minutes, then repeat the three blasts.
- Following the same pattern as with whistles, use two rocks or sticks to make a loud noise in groups of three.
- Lie down flat in a clearing to make the largest visible image for search aircraft. Do everything you can to draw attention to yourself.

ROADSIDE SIGNALS

If you are stranded on the side of a road, you can use these signals to indicate that you need help:

- Lift up both the hood and trunk of your car.
- Wave both hands wildly so your signal is not mistaken as a friendly wave.
- Point at passing cars with one hand, while you make the other hand the shape of a telephone receiver at your ear. Mouth the word, "Help." This should alert passing motorists to call for help on their cell phones or CB radios. If you are stranded in your car in a remote area you can try any of the other land emergency signals.

Universal Sign for Needing Assistance

If you have no way to call for help, tie a bright red piece of cloth on your car's antenna. This is the universal sign for needing assistance. Always let someone know what time you departed for and what time you expect to arrive at your destination.

SIGNALS IF YOU ARE LOST

If you are lost, staying put and using signals is your best course. If you cannot wait for help, then do the following:

- Go downhill.
- Look for rivers, ravines, or roads, then follow them.
- Travel in a straight line.

SELF-RELIANCE

Former Secretary of Agriculture and church leader Ezra Taft Benson challenged us to be self-sustaining through adequate preparation. "An almost forgotten means of economic self-reliance is the home production of food. We are too accustomed to going to stores and purchasing what we need. By producing some of our food we reduce, to a great extent, the impact of inflation on our money." And author Esther Dickey reminds, "Use it up, wear it out, make it do, or do without."

EVACUATION PLAN

Make a map of your home and include the following:

- Label every exit, including doors, windows, and hallways.
- In every room, label the primary exit (usually a door or hallway) and a secondary exit (usually a window).
- Label every room in which a family member sleeps.
- Label the main valves for gas, electricity and water lines.
- Establish a safe meeting place outside the home so everyone can be accounted for.

LOCAL EVACUATION PLANS

According to FEMA (the Federal Emergency Management Agency), you should contact your local emergency management or civil defense office to find out the evacuation plans for your own area. Be sure to listen to television or radio broadcasts at the time of an emergency.

POST A MESSAGE

Before you leave, tie a piece of white cloth to your front door or mailbox to let authorities know you have evacuated. Or prominently post a message on your front door, listing family members, the time you evacuated, and your evacuation destination and alternate destination.

EVACUATION PRACTICE TIME

No evacuation plan will work well unless it is practiced on a regular basis.

- Everyone in the family should to learn how to escape. Teach children how to escape out windows in case they cannot exit through a door. You may want to arrange dressers or night stands to be under windows for easier escape.

- Store 72-hour kits strategically near exits. When you practice, assign certain family members to be in charge of grabbing the 72-hour kits.

- Practice turning off utility valves.

- Incorporate other life-saving habits such as always leaving a pair of shoes and a flashlight at each person's bedside.

- Practice with saving time in mind.

- Practice your plan at least four times each year and adjust your plan according to the ages of family members.

USE SIMPLICITY IN YOUR EMERGENCY PLAN

Family preparedness plans should be simple enough for people to remember key details. A plan that is too detailed will not be effective. Keep in mind that under stress people tend to get confused, and the fewer the details they have to remember, the better the plan will work.

HOUSE ADDRESS NUMBER

Make sure your house address number can be easily and clearly seen from the street both day and night. Your number should be prominently posted on your house.

INDIVIDUALS WITH SPECIAL NEEDS

In developing your emergency plans, always remember individuals with specials needs, such as infants, small children, the ill, the elderly, the disabled, and those living alone.

INVENTORY

Conduct an inventory of your home, garage, premises, and places of business. Make a complete written itemized list of all the contents. You may want to use a tape recorder or camera to take the inventory. Duplicates of your inventory, as well as duplicates of important documents and vital family records, should be kept in a location outside of your home. A duplicate copy of your family "Emergency and Evacuation Plan" should be in each family member's 72-hour kit.

HELP OTHERS TO PREPARE

Help educate others to realize the importance of prudent planning and preparing.

- Prepare your immediate family, and pass along pointers and information to extended family, friends, and neighbors.
- Take classes in first aid and emergency care from your local Red Cross or fire department.
- Help establish community watch groups to safeguard your community against crime.
- Become familiar with the elderly or sick in your area who may need added assistance in an emergency situation.
- Work with your local PTA and government groups to know their plans and to voice your needs and concerns.
- Make suggestions to leaders of your church, clubs, or interest groups to make sure they have emergency resources and plans.

SAFETY CHECK YOUR HOME

Some things you should check in your home:

- Keep your main gas valve (usually located near the outside meter) free of obstructions such as overgrown trees and bushes and trash.

- Keep a nonsparking shutoff wrench near the main gas valve.
- Label your electrical circuits.
- Repair electrical wiring according to local building codes.
- Check all electrical outlets to make sure they are not overloaded with too many electrical appliances.
- Place fire extinguishers that will handle different types of fires in strategic areas of your home (kitchen, garage, etc.).
- Install a smoke detector in every bedroom of your home, checking the batteries regularly.
- Keep your furnace area clear of combustible materials.
- Properly dispose of opened containers of combustible materials and any rags used for painting or refinishing.

DISASTER PREPAREDNESS INSIGHTS AND TIPS

EARTHQUAKES

Earthquakes are natural disasters that we cannot fully predict. But we can make preparations to help minimize the trauma they cause and help maximize odds for survival. According to the Red Cross, here is some valuable information.

What to Do During an Earthquake

- STAY CALM.

- If you are indoors, stay indoors. The most dangerous thing to do during an earthquake is to try to leave the building. Objects can fall on you. Use the "DUCK, COVER, and HOLD" drill. DUCK or drop down on the floor. Take COVER under a sturdy desk, table, or other furniture. If that is not possible, seek cover against an interior wall and protect your head and neck with your arms. Avoid windows, hanging objects, mirrors, or tall furniture. If you take cover under a sturdy piece of furniture, HOLD on to it and be prepared to move with it. Hold the position until the ground stops shaking and it is safe to move.

- If you are outside, move to an open area away from trees, buildings, signs, streetlights, and utility wires. Lie flat on the ground. Do not try to run. Do not go underground or into a tunnel. Do not try to go into a building. Stay outside until the shaking stops. Remember, aftershocks are often more destructive than initial shocks.

- If you are in a car, stop quickly and stay put. Don't get out. When the shaking stops, proceed with caution. Drive to an open area away from buildings, trees, overpasses, or utility wires. Avoid bridges or ramps that might have sustained damage.

- If you are in a multiple-level building, DUCK under a desk or table until the quaking stops. Or lean against an interior wall. COVER your head and neck with your arms. Do not use elevators to evacuate. Use the stairs with caution; they will likely be filled with panicking people.

- If you are on a sidewalk, hide in the arch of a doorway to protect yourself from falling bricks, glass, plaster and other debris.

- If you are in a public building such as a store, step away from displays that contain objects that could fall. DUCK under a table or some other sturdy object. Do not run to an exit until the shaking is over, and then proceed with caution.

What to Do After an Earthquake

1. Find family members. Meet at your predetermined meeting place(s). Call your family's out-of-the-area contact person, whose name and numbers should be memorized by each person.

2. Check for injuries and provide first aid. Contact emergency professionals as soon as possible.

3. Check for gas, water, and sewage breaks; check for downed

electric lines and shorts; turn off appropriate utilities; check for building damage and potential safety problems during aftershocks, such as cracks around chimney and foundation.

4. Clean up dangerous spills, broken glass, and jagged wood.

5. Don't use matches or fire of any kind until you are sure that there are no gas leaks or flammable chemical spills nearby. Flashlights should be turned on outside before bringing them inside. A light stick is the safest source of light.

6. Do not drink from the faucet until authorities pronounce it safe to do so. All water should be purified or filtered before drinking because it could have become contaminated. Ration your water sensibly, but not to the point that you become dehydrated.

7. Turn on the radio and listen for instructions from public safety agencies.

8. Do not enter any damaged buildings. Cautiously inspect your home for damage. If it is unsafe to enter, go to the nearest shelter or to the home of a friend in a safe location. Take your 72-hour kit with you. Let emergency services know where you are.

9. Don't use the telephone except for emergency use.

10. Get ready for aftershocks that often take place following an earthquake. Aftershocks can be very damaging and can occur hours, days, weeks, or even months after the initial quake.

11. Wear thick-soled shoes or boots.

Fourteen Survival Items to Keep on Hand

1. Portable radio with extra batteries

2. Flashlight with extra batteries

3. First aid kit, including specific medicines needed by members of your household

4. First aid book

5. Fire extinguisher

6. Adjustable wrench for turning off gas and water

7. Smoke detector, properly installed

8. Portable fire escape ladder for homes/apartments with multiple floors

9. Potable water in an amount sufficient for the number of members in your household

10. Portable food supply sufficient for at least 72 hours for each member of your household. NOTE: Both water and food should be rotated into normal meals of household to keep freshness.

11. Manual can opener

12. Portable stove with necessary fuel. NOTE: Such stoves should not be used until it is determined that there is no gas leak in the area.

13. Fire starters

14. Telephone numbers of police, fire department, and doctor, and an out-of-the-area friend as a contact person whom all family members can call

Three Things You Need to Know

1. How to turn off gas, water, and electricity

2. First aid procedures

3. How to reunite your family in first- and second-choice meeting places, and the name and telephone number of an out-of-the-area contact person whom all family members can call

The best survival is a prepared survival. Hold regular drills with your family and also discuss various scenarios, such as what you would do if everyone were at work and school when an earthquake occurs. Proper preparation certainly brings peace of mind and minimizes chaos.

The Home Earthquake Hazard Hunt

You can identify earthquake dangers in your home by conducting an earthquake hazard hunt. Go from room to room and imagine what could happen during an earthquake. Here are some possible hazards:

- **Beds next to large windows**—The glass could shatter and harm those who are asleep.

- **Beds directly below shelves or hanging lights**—The lights or objects on shelves could fall on those below.

- **Beds below heavy mirrors or framed pictures**—Heavy objects on the walls can easily fall during an earthquake.

- **Heavy lamps on bedside tables**—These could fall and injure people. Fasten lamps securely to tables or replace heavy lamps with light, non-breakable lamps.

- **Hanging plants in heavy pots**—The heavier the pot the more likely it is to fall or tip over.

- **Open-ended hooks holding hanging plants, lamps, and other objects**—The force of an earthquake can make such items swing right off their hooks.

- **Fasteners that are not anchored in studs**—An earthquake could shake such unsecured fasteners right out of the wall, causing the objects that they support to fall.

- **Breakable or heavy objects on shelves**—They can fall and break on the floor. Consider a cabinet with latching doors, instead of shelves.

- **Loose latches (such as magnetic latches) on cabinets and cupboards**—Such cabinets could swing open during an earthquake, causing the contents to spill out. Replace them with new locking latches.

- **Glass bottles in medicine cabinets**—Place glass containers on lower shelves or at the back of medicine cabinets. Some shelves have a shelf railing to prevent items from falling off. (PARENTS NOTE: For your child's safety, make sure you use childproof latches when you move things to lower shelves.)

- **Glass containers around the bathtub**—Could easily break.
- **Flammable materials close to heat sources**—Painting or cleaning products should be stored in the garage or outside in a shed. Newspaper or cardboard should be recycled or thrown away.
- **Heavy or glass objects next to the exits or escape routes in your house**—You won't be able to move them and escape when you need to.
- **Objects with wheels**—Such objects could roll during an earthquake. Block the wheels so the object cannot roll.
- **Tall, heavy furniture (such as bookshelves and china cabinets)**—Attach such furniture securely to the studs in the walls.
- **Heavy appliances such as refrigerators**—These should be secured to the studs in the walls.
- **Water heaters**—These should be attached to studs in the wall or secured by a water heater support system.
- **Dead or diseased tree limbs**—They could fall from trees and damage your house or injure people.
- **Inflexible connectors where gas lines meet appliances, such as stoves, water heaters, and dryers**—Stress could cause the connection to break and flood your home with toxic, explosive gas.
- **Air conditioners**—Make sure they are braced well.
- **Roof tiles**—Make sure they are secure. Fix loose tiles.
- **Chimney**—Nail plywood to ceiling joists in the attic to protect from bricks that could fall through the ceiling.

FIRE

Smoke Alarms

Your home's fire protection should start with smoke detectors. If you are asleep when a fire starts, you will not smell the smoke because the poisonous gases in the smoke will cause you to fall into an even deeper sleep. During a fire, a smoke alarm will sound to wake you and give you time to escape. Placing several smoke alarms in your home cuts the risk of death from a residential fire in half. But even if you have smoke alarms, you must ensure that they work properly.

- Clean your smoke alarm monthly.
- Test your smoke alarm monthly by using the test button or introducing smoke into the unit.
- Place a smoke alarm outside each bedroom and on every level of your home, including the basement.
- Make sure everyone in your home can hear the alarm even when bedroom doors are shut.
- Install a smoke alarm inside your bedroom if you sleep with the bedroom doors closed or if you use heaters or other electrical appliances in your room.
- Mount smoke alarms high on a wall or on the ceiling because smoke rises.
- Do not borrow batteries from smoke alarms and use them for another purpose.
- Do not install a smoke alarm near a window or door where drafts could interfere with the detector's operation.

Fire Drill

In case of a fire, you should have a plan to get your family out of the house. Choose a safe place for everyone to meet, far enough away from the house to be out of harm's way. At the end of the drill, have children pretend to run to a neighbor's house to call 9-1-1. (But don't actually call.) Practice this drill often. See if you can improve on your time.

Stop, Drop, and Roll!

Each time you practice the fire drill, teach your children what to do if their clothes catch on fire. You can start by having the children walk or run in place. At your signal, have them immediately stop, drop to the ground, and roll until the "flames" are out. As they practice this exercise, "stop, drop, and roll" will become an automatic response for them.

Primary and Secondary Exits of Your Home

Family members should know how to escape in case of an emergency. Draw a map of your house and include the following:

- Every exit, including doors, windows, and hallways
- The main shut off points of the gas, electricity, and water lines
- The room each family member sleeps in
- The best exits from each room of your house
- A place to meet outside the home, immediately upon evacuation

FLOOD

Here are some rules to keep in mind.

- Listen to weather reports to find out if there is a flash flood watch, warning, or advisory. A "flash flood watch" means that the weather forecasters expect a flash flood, but one hasn't occurred yet. In this case you should prepare to evacuate when ordered by authorities. A "flash flood warning" means there is some actual damage occurring. A "flash flood advisory" means that flooding is in progress. In a warning or an advisory, you should immediately seek high ground and keep the following rules in mind.

- Do not try to walk through floodwaters. Even six inches of fast-moving water can knock you off your feet.
- Do not try to drive forward through floodwaters. The road

could be washed out. Your car could be carried away. If you can safely back up, drive another way to higher ground.

- If your car stalls, leave it and walk safely to higher ground.
- Take extra precautions at night since flood dangers are more difficult to see in the dark.

Flood Clean-up Rules

- Never eat food that has been in floodwater. Discard it immediately. Floodwater is usually contaminated with sewage and other garbage.
- Don't drink untreated floodwater. If you use well water, have your well flushed and tested before using it. Your local sanitation department can give you instructions. If you must use floodwater for drinking water, purify or filter it. (See "The Importance of Water," p. 17)
- Wear long-sleeve shirts and long pants to avoid being cut by flood debris. If you do get cut, wash the area with soap and clean water before bandaging it.
- If caught in floodwaters, make sure you wash your hands and body thoroughly, especially before eating or putting things in your mouth.

HURRICANES

Many choose to ignore evacuation notices and try to wait it out, often with fatal results. Be wise! Usually you will have only a 24-hour notice if a hurricane is threatening your area. As a preparation and for insurance purposes, you should inventory all of your possessions in your home. You should take photographs of the exterior of your home and all the interior rooms.

The major cause of death during a hurricane is drowning, so stay indoors and away from the water. The "eye of the storm" can be deceiving. At the storm's center all can be calm. Sometimes people believe they are safe. But a dangerous part of the storm is coming. Stay inside until official reporting stations confirm that the storm has passed.

Preparation

- Plan an evacuation route. Have a backup plan.
- Know how to find nearby shelters.
- Store disaster supplies such as:

  Flashlight and extra batteries

  Portable, battery-operated, solar, or hand-crank radio and extra batteries

  First aid kit and manual

  Emergency food and water

  Leather gloves and boots

  Pry bar or crow bar

  Essential medications, cash, credit cards, sturdy shoes, warm clothing, sleeping bag, etc. (See Chapter Two for a more complete list.)

- Fill your automobile gas tank.
- Teach family members how to respond before, during, and after a hurricane.
- Teach family members how to turn off gas, electricity, and water.
- Have a contact person outside of the area to whom family members can report their whereabouts and condition.
- Teach children how and when to call 9–1–1 and how to tune the radio for emergency information.
- Protect your windows. Permanent shutters offer the best protection. Plywood panels cut to fit the window are a good, low-cost option. Taping windows with masking tape in an "X" pattern can help.
- Trim back dead or weak branches from surrounding trees.
- Consider purchasing flood or natural disaster insurance.

During a Hurricane Watch

- Tune into the radio or television for reports.
- Check emergency supplies.
- Store valuables and important papers in a watertight container in the highest level of your home.
- Fill your car's gas tank with fuel.
- Bring lawn furniture, toys, and garden tools inside. Anchor furniture that cannot be brought inside.
- Close and board windows.
- Turn refrigerator to coldest setting and open only when necessary. (This will help to preserve food if the power shuts off.)
- Store drinking water.
- Review evacuation plan.
- Avoid using elevators.
- Avoid open flames as a source of light.
- If power goes off, shut off main switch to avoid a surge when power is restored.

If Evacuation Becomes Necessary

Although it is best to stay indoors during a hurricane, there are times when the threat of danger is so great that evacuation becomes essential.

- Secure home by turning off gas, electricity, and water.
- Have a central meeting place to gather family members.
- Tell someone where you are going.
- Lock your home and leave.
- Bring preassembled emergency supplies and warm protective clothing.
- Take blankets and sleeping bags to a predetermined emergency shelter.

After a Hurricane Has Passed

- Stay tuned to radio and TV for important updates and warnings.
- Help injured or trapped people.
- Give first aid when appropriate and call emergency professionals for help.
- Return home only after authorities say it is safe.
- Avoid loose or dangling power lines; report them immediately.
- Reenter home with caution.
- Beware of snakes, insects, and animals driven to higher ground by flood waters.
- Ventilate home.
- Check refrigerated or frozen foods for spoilage.
- Use telephone only for emergency calls to keep lines open.
- Take pictures of damage for insurance claims.
- Drive only if necessary and avoid flooded roads or washed-out bridges.
- Check for gas leaks. If you smell gas or hear a blowing or hissing noise, open a window and quickly leave the building!
- Look for electrical system damage. If you see sparks or broken or frayed wires, or if you smell hot insulation, turn off the main fuse box or circuit breaker and call an electrician.
- Check for sewer- and water-line damage. If you suspect damage, avoid using these lines and contact a plumber.

Lightning

When Lightning Strikes

If you are caught outdoors when a lightning storm hits, get away from the following:

- Open bodies of water
- Metal objects (including vehicles, fences, pipes, rails)
- Crowds of people
- Trees
- Telephone poles

Go to the lowest—not the highest—point on the ground. Make sure you are not the tallest object in the vicinity. If you are in an open field, drop to your knees and bend forward with your hands on your knees. You should NOT lie flat on the ground. Be especially cautious if your hair starts feeling like it's "standing on end." This could be a warning that lightning is about to target YOU!

TORNADOES

Here are some basic ideas to protect yourself in a tornado:

- Go to a safe place: a storm shelter, a basement, or a low-lying area.
- Go into a hall and get on your knees. Put your head on the floor facing an interior wall. Fold your arms over the back of your head.
- Stay away from windows.
- If a shelter is not available, get in a bathtub and cover yourself with a mattress.
- If you are in a mobile home, get out. Go to another person's basement or storm shelter.
- If you are outdoors and no shelter is available, lie flat on the ground. But do not lie in a drainage ditch or stream bed. Flash floods often accompany tornadoes.
- **What to do after a tornado**—Follow the instructions listed in "What to Do after an Earthquake."

CHAPTER NINE

CONCLUDING THOUGHTS

Get Started Now

The following statement was issued by Tom Ridge, Homeland Security Secretary, and R. David Paulison, U.S. Fire Administrator:

"Have on hand three days' worth of water and food, an emergency supply kit for both home and automobile, radios with extra batteries, and plastic sheeting and duct tape to seal windows and doors . . . Make a plan for contacting family members in an emergency. Be especially aware of your surroundings and the events happening around you."

In this book we have tried to address basic tips for preparedness. Most of these tips reflect common sense. We hope we have added to your understanding and your motivation to get started.

THE FIRST THREE DAYS

The first three days following any disaster are the most crucial. That is the time that emergency services are likely to be unavailable or that you will have to wait for rescue. The wrong time to become educated is during an emergency.

WATER

Water storage, purification, filtration, and knowledge could mean the difference between life and death. You can live only a few days without clean water.

FOOD

Food storage is as important as a savings account. You can't eat money. You can't buy food that is not on a store shelf. Learning to use your storage is a priority. No one wants to abruptly modify his diet. In the best of times it can cause stress; in the worst of times it can be unhealthy.

WARMTH, SHELTER, AND CLOTHING

Your ability to stay warm and find shelter is critical to your survival. Some clothing materials that you think will keep you warm can actually jeopardize your life. A modest shelter can shield you from life-threatening elements.

LIGHT, TOOLS, AND COMMUNICATIONS

A preparedness plan is useless if it does not include proper tools such as alternative sources of light and communication. If you can't see, you can't work your plan. If you don't know what is going on in the outside world, you are isolated and vulnerable. If you can't locate family members, panic sets in and unwise decisions may be made.

FIRST AID AND SANITATION

A basic knowledge of first aid, a good first aid kit, and a reference book can turn around a critical situation and buy precious time while you wait for medical professionals to arrive. Sanitation knowledge has halted the spread of disease in disaster episodes.

Emergency preparedness is for everyone. People who have prepared become voices of calm and assurance in times of natural disasters, accidents, and conflicts. They and their families achieve a sense of security. None of us wants a disaster to happen; we only hope that if it does we will be prepared. May we all live by this advice: "Plan for the worst and expect the best."